LEARNING STRATEGIES CURRICULUM

D1484707

The Fundamentals of Paraphrasing and Summarizing

STUDENT MATERIALS

Jim Knight, Ph.D.
Jean B. Schumaker, Ph.D.
2007

Managing Editor: Jacqueline Schafer
Cover Design: Mike Bingham
Copy Editor: Kirsten McBride

CONTENTS

CONTENTS

(continued)

INTRODUCTION

The Learning Sheets in this book are designed to be used in conjunction with instruction that is described in the instructor's manual for the *Fundamentals in Paraphrasing and Summarizing* program.* They are not designed to be used in absence of this instruction, nor are they to be used without regard for mastery learning. That is, if students are expected to learn the concepts and skills associated with these materials, they must receive feedback about their performance after each practice attempt, and they must be required to practice the skills associated with each lesson until they reach mastery as described in the instructor's manual. Students who have mastered the skills at each level are to proceed to additional instruction, to help other students, or to work on other tasks until their peers have met mastery. Asking them to complete additional learning sheets of the same type will probably result in decreased motivation to strive for mastery of new skills.

The following list shows the skills that students will learn associated with each set of Learning Sheets:

Lesson 1 Learning Sheets: Paraphrasing Words
Lesson 2 Learning Sheets: Paraphrasing Phrases
Lesson 3 Learning Sheets: Paraphrasing Sentences
Lesson 4 Learning Sheets: Identifying Topics, Main Ideas, and Details
Lesson 5 Learning Sheets: Identifying Details When Given the Topic and Main Idea
Lesson 6 Learning Sheets: Identifying Details in Paragraphs
Lesson 7 Learning Sheets: Identifying Topics, Main Ideas, and Details in Paragraphs
Lesson 8 Learning Sheets: Paraphrasing the Main Idea and Details
Lesson 9 Learning Sheets: Paraphrasing Multiple Paragraphs
Lesson 10 Learning Sheets: Creating Topics and Main Ideas from Details
Lesson 11 Learning Sheets: Identifying and Paraphrasing Details, Main Ideas, and Topics
Lesson 12 Learning Sheets: Paraphrasing Passages When Main Ideas Are Not Clear
Lesson 13 Learning Sheets: Practicing Paraphrasing
Lesson 14 Learning Sheets: Generalizing to Standardized Tests

Permission is granted to the owner of this book to copy the Learning Sheets for personal use in providing instruction to students learning the fundamental skills associated with paraphrasing and summarizing. Copying these lesson materials for other instructors or for any other purpose in any form is in violation of copyright law.

---

* Schumaker, J. B., Knight, J., & Deshler, D. D. (2007) *Fundamentals of paraphrasing and summarizing: Instructor's manual*. Lawrence, KS: Edge Enterprises, Inc.

Pretest Passage

Name _____

Date _____

INSTRUCTIONS:
First, identify an appropriate main idea, topic, and relevant details for each paragraph. Then, paraphrase the main idea and two of the details for each paragraph on a _Paraphrasing Sheet_.

Mother Teresa: Inspiring the World to Love

Agnes Bojaxhiu was born in 1910 in Kosovo. She never became an athlete, a singer, or the leader of a country, but she grew to be one of the great heroes of the 20th century. Agnes was raised by her single mother, Drana. Her father died when she was 9 years old. Her mother's kind and firm teachings led Agnes to become a light of hope for thousands of poor people in the world. Agnes's mother worked hard, sewing and selling wedding dresses, making embroidery, and working at night. As busy as she was, Drana also prayed every evening with her children, and taught them the importance of charity work. Agnes helped her mother care for the poor, needy, and helpless people in their community. Agnes decided that she wanted to spend her life helping others. When she was 18, she left her home to become a teacher. Years later, the young woman became famous around the world as Mother Teresa.

Mother Teresa moved to Calcutta, India, to teach. Her young students loved her kindness and enthusiasm. She taught from 1929 until 1948. However, she could not ignore the many poor people she saw in the streets of the city. In 1946, she began to work among them. To help with her work, she sought money from churches and other groups. In 1950, she created The Missionaries of Charity. The goal of her group was to care for the poor, sick, and forgotten people of Calcutta. The Missionaries of Charity grew to involve more than 1,000 people in India. Mother Teresa brought together doctors, social workers, and nurses to help those who most needed it. The group was just the start of the great work she did in India.

Mother Teresa did many great things during her life in India. She created more than 50 relief programs across the country. She created clinics and many homes for children, lepers, and the dying. Her work made her famous around the world. In 1963, she received a great honor in India for her work with the people of the country. In 1971, she was awarded the Pope John XXIII Peace Prize. In 1979, she won the Nobel Peace Prize. Perhaps Mother Teresa is most famous for inspiring people to help those who are most in need. By giving her life to others, Mother Teresa led thousands to great acts of kindness. Mother Teresa taught the world how to give love, respect, and care to everyone in the world.

Learning Sheet 1A

Paraphrasing Words

Name _____

Date _____

INSTRUCTIONS:
Paraphrase each word by writing it in your own words in the space provided.

EXAMPLES:

Awful _____terrible_____ Frequently _____often_____ Piece _____bit_____

LEARN BY WATCHING

C

☐	1.	Talk	_____
☐	2.	Hurry	_____
☐	3.	Ancient	_____

LEARN BY SHARING

C

☐	1.	Beautiful	_____
☐	2.	Disappear	_____
☐	3.	Accuse	_____
☐	4.	Garbage	_____
☐	5.	Gigantic	_____

LEARN BY PRACTICING

C

Point

☐	1.	Begin	_____	☐
☐	2.	Assist	_____	☐
☐	3.	Silly	_____	☐
☐	4.	Tidy	_____	☐
☐	5.	Weep	_____	☐

Learning Sheet 1B

Paraphrasing Words

INSTRUCTIONS:
Paraphrase each word by writing it in your own words in the space provided.

EXAMPLES:

Battle _____ *fight* _____   Lonesome _____ *lonely* _____   Blizzard _____ *storm* _____

LEARN BY WATCHING

C

☐	1.	Tardy
☐	2.	Kind
☐	3.	Sleepy

LEARN BY SHARING

C

☐	1.	House
☐	2.	Joyful
☐	3.	Modern
☐	4.	Understand
☐	5.	Active

LEARN BY PRACTICING

C

Points

☐	1.	Make	☐
☐	2.	Modify	☐
☐	3.	Many	☐
☐	4.	Blaring	☐
☐	5.	Evening	☐

Learning Sheet 1C

Paraphrasing Words

Name _____

Date _____

INSTRUCTIONS:
Paraphrase each word by writing it in your own words in the space provided.

EXAMPLES:

Ache _____pain_____ Easy _____simple_____ Respond _____answer_____

LEARN BY WATCHING

C

☐	1.	**Task**	_____
☐	2.	**Dazzling**	_____
☐	3.	**Gain**	_____

LEARN BY SHARING

C

☐	1.	**Beneficial**	_____
☐	2.	**Purchase**	_____
☐	3.	**Shadowy**	_____
☐	4.	**Parched**	_____
☐	5.	**Jubilant**	_____

LEARN BY PRACTICING

C

Point

☐	1.	**Playmate**	_____	☐
☐	2.	**Thrilling**	_____	☐
☐	3.	**Sad**	_____	☐
☐	4.	**Precious**	_____	☐
☐	5.	**Rescue**	_____	☐

Learning Sheet 1D

Paraphrasing Words

Name _____

Date _____

INSTRUCTIONS:
Paraphrase each word by writing it in your own words in the space provided.

EXAMPLES:

Task _____job_____ Alike _____similar_____ Bad _____nasty_____

LEARN BY WATCHING

C

☐	1.	**Mistake** _____
☐	2.	**Seize** _____
☐	3.	**Economical** _____

LEARN BY SHARING

C

☐	1.	**Yell** _____
☐	2.	**Intelligent** _____
☐	3.	**Vacant** _____
☐	4.	**Crowded** _____
☐	5.	**Acquire** _____

LEARN BY PRACTICING

C

Points

☐	1.	**Wish** _____	☐
☐	2.	**Leap** _____	☐
☐	3.	**Money** _____	☐
☐	4.	**Peaceful** _____	☐
☐	5.	**Final** _____	☐

Learning Sheet 2A

Paraphrasing Phrases

Name _____

Date _____

INSTRUCTIONS:
Paraphrase each phrase by writing it in your own words in the space provided.

EXAMPLE:
a cool dude _____*a nice guy*_____

LEARN BY WATCHING

C   O   M

☐ ☐ ☐   1. lovely sketches
_____

☐ ☐ ☐   2. beside my mother
_____

☐ ☐ ☐   3. along the avenue
_____

LEARN BY SHARING

C   O   M

☐ ☐ ☐   1. the giant automobile
_____

☐ ☐ ☐   2. a chilly wind
_____

☐ ☐ ☐   3. a frightening event
_____

LEARN BY PRACTICING

C   O   M   Poin

☐ ☐ ☐   1. regulations prohibit   ☐
_____

☐ ☐ ☐   2. my greatest desire   ☐
_____

☐ ☐ ☐   3. startled by the sound   ☐
_____

☐ ☐ ☐   4. where dinner is prepared   ☐
_____

☐ ☐ ☐   5. after the movie   ☐
_____

Learning Sheet 2B

Paraphrasing Phrases

Name _____

Date _____

INSTRUCTIONS:
Paraphrase each phrase by writing it in your own words in the space provided.

EXAMPLE:

Several adaptations   *many changes*

LEARN BY WATCHING

C   O   M

☐ ☐ ☐ 1. defeat our opponents
_____

☐ ☐ ☐ 2. the steamy night
_____

☐ ☐ ☐ 3. a difficult assignment
_____

LEARN BY SHARING

C   O   M

☐ ☐ ☐ 1. a dull ache
_____

☐ ☐ ☐ 2. a pleasant melody
_____

☐ ☐ ☐ 3. a kind young woman
_____

LEARN BY PRACTICING

C   O   M   Points

☐ ☐ ☐ 1. a thrilling book   ☐
_____

☐ ☐ ☐ 2. an ugly serpent   ☐
_____

☐ ☐ ☐ 3. the chilly time of year   ☐
_____

☐ ☐ ☐ 4. a complicated thought   ☐
_____

☐ ☐ ☐ 5. the evening TV show   ☐
_____

Learning Sheet 2C

Paraphrasing Phrases

Name _____

Date _____

INSTRUCTIONS:
Paraphrase each phrase by writing it in your own words in the space provided.

EXAMPLE:

a soft voice _____a whisper_____

LEARN BY WATCHING

C   O   M

☐ ☐ ☐   1. wild beast
_____

☐ ☐ ☐   2. lonely melody
_____

☐ ☐ ☐   3. labored diligently
_____

LEARN BY SHARING

C   O   M

☐ ☐ ☐   1. the responsible party
_____

☐ ☐ ☐   2. something unexpected
_____

☐ ☐ ☐   3. amazing experience
_____

LEARN BY PRACTICING

C   O   M   Poin

☐ ☐ ☐   1. swift runner   ☐
_____

☐ ☐ ☐   2. tiny shrub   ☐
_____

☐ ☐ ☐   3. delicious supper   ☐
_____

☐ ☐ ☐   4. a cheerful young woman ☐
_____

☐ ☐ ☐   5. steaming beverage   ☐
_____

Learning Sheet 2D

Paraphrasing Phrases

Name _____

Date _____

INSTRUCTIONS:
Paraphrase each phrase by writing it in your own words in the space provided.

EXAMPLE:

a kind young woman   _a nice girl_____

LEARN BY WATCHING

C   O   M

☐   ☐   ☐   1. embrace my friend
_____

☐   ☐   ☐   2. plans for the future
_____

☐   ☐   ☐   3. remove your footware
_____

LEARN BY SHARING

C   O   M

☐   ☐   ☐   1. harmless to pets
_____

☐   ☐   ☐   2. a wonderful aroma
_____

☐   ☐   ☐   3. a large meal
_____

LEARN BY PRACTICING

C   O   M   Points

☐   ☐   ☐   1. the room where we watch TV   ☐
_____

☐   ☐   ☐   2. an amazing dream   ☐
_____

☐   ☐   ☐   3. the correct reply   ☐
_____

☐   ☐   ☐   4. more cheerful than the others   ☐
_____

☐   ☐   ☐   5. a fierce beast   ☐
_____

9

Learning Sheet 3A

Name _____

Date _____

Paraphrasing Sentences

INSTRUCTIONS:
Paraphrase each sentence by writing it in your own words in the space provided.

EXAMPLE:

The boy was overjoyed.   _The young man was exceedingly happy._

LEARN BY WATCHING

C   O   M

☐ ☐ ☐   1. I am determined to go to college when I complete high school.
_____

☐ ☐ ☐   2. If I exert myself, I know I can accomplish a lot.
_____

☐ ☐ ☐   3. The highway into the city was slippery.
_____

LEARN BY SHARING

C   O   M

☐ ☐ ☐   1. You can gain a lot of knowledge from articles on the Internet.
_____

☐ ☐ ☐   2. Rachel is not comfortable walking alone at night.
_____

☐ ☐ ☐   3. This semester, I am going to improve my scores on tests.
_____

LEARN BY PRACTICING

C   O   M   Poir

☐ ☐ ☐   1. Phillip took a hike along the riverbank.   ☐
_____

☐ ☐ ☐   2. Lekisha assisted Tom with his homework.   ☐
_____

☐ ☐ ☐   3. The food in the lunchroom tasted like plastic and paper.   ☐
_____

☐ ☐ ☐   4. Angel earned the highest grade on the test.   ☐
_____

☐ ☐ ☐   5. Millie spends an hour a day doing laps in the pool.   ☐
_____

10

Learning Sheet 3B
Paraphrasing Sentences

Name _____

Date _____

INSTRUCTIONS:
Paraphrase each sentence by writing it in your own words in the space provided.

> **EXAMPLE:**
>
> I enjoy completing projects with Bianca.   <u>I like working with Bianca.</u>

LEARN BY WATCHING

C   O   M

☐ ☐ ☐   1. The fireworks were spectacular last evening.
_____

☐ ☐ ☐   2. The sprinters raced at an amazing speed.
_____

☐ ☐ ☐   3. The automobile rumbled and roared at the stoplight.
_____

LEARN BY SHARING

C   O   M

☐ ☐ ☐   1. My father was an outstanding quarterback when he went to college.
_____

☐ ☐ ☐   2. Tonight, I am going to ignore TV and spend the night with a good book.
_____

☐ ☐ ☐   3. Respect is gained and given by taking the time to listen with great care.
_____

LEARN BY PRACTICING

C   O   M   Points

☐ ☐ ☐   1. On July 4, we celebrate the founding of the United States.   ☐
_____

☐ ☐ ☐   2. Tasha and Susan wore the same t-shirt and jeans to school yesterday. ☐
_____

☐ ☐ ☐   3. At sunrise, the sky was filled with reds, yellows, and blues.   ☐
_____

☐ ☐ ☐   4. Russia is the only country larger than Canada.   ☐
_____

☐ ☐ ☐   5. The coach inspired the team to hustle harder during the big game.   ☐
_____

Learning Sheet 3C

Paraphrasing Sentences

Name _____

Date _____

INSTRUCTIONS:

Paraphrase each sentence by writing it in your own words in the space provided.

EXAMPLE:

I adore the flavor of chocolate chip cookies. *I love the taste of chocolate chip cookies.*

LEARN BY WATCHING

C   O   M

☐ ☐ ☐   1. I throw away too much cash on useless items.

☐ ☐ ☐   2. After Tom started going to the gym, he discovered he had more get-up and go.

☐ ☐ ☐   3. Bob muttered to himself as he pushed the lawn mower all over the yard.

LEARN BY SHARING

C   O   M

☐ ☐ ☐   1. Mary was miserable when she discovered she had misplaced her assignment.

☐ ☐ ☐   2. Tom refused to talk about his classmates.

☐ ☐ ☐   3. My dog destroyed many of my possessions when I left him at my house alone.

LEARN BY PRACTICING

C   O   M   Points

☐ ☐ ☐   1. My father encouraged me to complete my tasks before watching TV.   ☐

☐ ☐ ☐   2. I was so keyed up about the big game that I stayed wide-awake until morning.   ☐

☐ ☐ ☐   3. The watercolor was vivid, interesting, and confusing.   ☐

☐ ☐ ☐   4. Susan's backpack was crammed with books and weighed a lot.   ☐

☐ ☐ ☐   5. At the library, I can make use of books, and I do not have to pay a penny.   ☐

Learning Sheet 3D

Paraphrasing Sentences

Name _____

Date _____

INSTRUCTIONS:
Paraphrase each sentence by writing it in your own words in the space provided.

EXAMPLE:

My favorite music is hip hop.   _I love hip hop music._

LEARN BY WATCHING

C   O   M

☐ ☐ ☐   1. My big truck does not drive as quickly as my friend's automobile.
_____

☐ ☐ ☐   2. I wish that my summer holiday lasted just a couple of more weeks longer.
_____

☐ ☐ ☐   3. Mary had a plan to be in great shape before the volleyball tryout.
_____

LEARN BY SHARING

C   O   M

☐ ☐ ☐   1. Jenny is one of the kindest people I know.
_____

☐ ☐ ☐   2. Some day in the future, I hope to travel to California.
_____

☐ ☐ ☐   3. Enthusiasm is sometimes more important than effort.
_____

LEARN BY PRACTICING

C   O   M   Points

☐ ☐ ☐   1. I find getting to school on time each day to be difficult.   ☐
_____

☐ ☐ ☐   2. My brother messes up the house every day.   ☐
_____

☐ ☐ ☐   3. Mary loves to read stories about teenagers who live exciting lives.   ☐
_____

☐ ☐ ☐   4. You can grow a good deal if you notice what happens when you make mistakes.   ☐
_____

☐ ☐ ☐   5. People who smoke waste their money and smell bad, too.   ☐
_____

Learning Sheet 4A

Identifying Topics, Main Ideas, and Details

Name _____

Date _____

INSTRUCTIONS:
Put a D beside each detail, a T beside each topic, and an M beside each main idea.

EXAMPLE:
<u>D</u>   The lead guitarist was fantastic.
<u>T</u>   The band.
<u>M</u>   The band played really well.
<u>D</u>   The drummer kept everyone playing right in time.

LEARN BY WATCHING

_____   Hockey gives me a chance to skate.

_____   I love the exercise I get when I play sports.

_____   Soccer gives me a chance to run a lot.

_____   Sports.

LEARN BY SHARING

_____   Acting is my favorite thing to do.

_____   Acting.

_____   Waiting back stage before the play starts is exciting.

_____   I love the sensation of everyone watching me on stage.

LEARN BY PRACTICING

Points

_____   Canadian chocolate bars.   ☐

_____   The Big Turk tastes like raspberry gum drops with chocolate.   ☐

_____   Caramilk has smooth, sweet, caramel inside.   ☐

_____   Canada has different chocolate bars than the U.S.   ☐

_____   What I do to make friends.   ☐

_____   I do not pretend to be someone I am not.   ☐

_____   Making friends.   ☐

_____   I accept everyone, not just those who are popular.   ☐

14

Learning Sheet 4B

Identifying Topics, Main Ideas, and Details

Name _____

Date _____

INSTRUCTIONS:
Put a D beside each detail, a T beside each topic, and an M beside each main idea.

EXAMPLE:	
D	The lead guitarist was fantastic.
T	The band.
M	The band played really well.
D	The drummer kept everyone playing right in time.

LEARN BY WATCHING

_____ I want to hike the Grand Canyon.

_____ I want to experience two vacations this year.

_____ I want to watch in the arena as my team wins the NBA final game.

_____ Vacations.

LEARN BY SHARING

_____ Computers do so many things.

_____ Computers.

_____ You can use them to communicate with people on the Internet.

_____ You can play awesome games.

LEARN BY PRACTICING

Points

_____ I never want to stumble on a bear in the forest. ☐

_____ Experiences. ☐

_____ I never want to forget to wear my pants to school. ☐

_____ I never want to have two terrifying experiences. ☐

_____ Reasons to go to college. ☐

_____ I have two reasons why I will go to college. ☐

_____ I will learn and get a little wisdom. ☐

_____ I will make more money. ☐

15

Learning Sheet 4C

Name _____

Date _____

Identifying Topics, Main Ideas, and Details

INSTRUCTIONS:
Put a D beside each detail, a T beside each topic, and an M beside each main idea.

EXAMPLE:

 D   The lead guitarist was fantastic.
 T   The band.
 M   The band played really well.
 D   The drummer kept everyone playing right in time.

LEARN BY WATCHING

_____   Poisonous snakes kill people.

_____   A few creatures are not likeable.

_____   Skunks smell awful.

_____   Frightening creatures.

LEARN BY SHARING

_____   We had a beautiful morning at my friend's cottage.

_____   We watched the sun come up over the lake.

_____   We went canoeing in the morning.

_____   Visiting my friend's cabin.

LEARN BY PRACTICING

Points

_____   Dan shares things with me.   ☐

_____   He listens to me when I feel a little unhappy.   ☐

_____   Dan is my best friend.   ☐

_____   Dan.   ☐

_____   What I would do if I were president.   ☐

_____   Being president.   ☐

_____   I would extend summer vacation by a month.   ☐

_____   I would pass some laws about the taste of school cafeteria food.   ☐

Learning Sheet 4D

Identifying Topics, Main Ideas, and Details

Name _____

Date _____

INSTRUCTIONS:
Put a D beside each detail, a T beside each topic, and an M beside each main idea.

EXAMPLE:
<u>D</u>   The lead guitarist was fantastic.
<u>T</u>   The band.
<u>M</u>   The band played really well.
<u>D</u>   The drummer kept everyone playing right in time.

LEARN BY WATCHING

_____   He carries a love letter everywhere.

_____   Objects.

_____   He also keeps an old banana peel.

_____   Objects that are in Bob's backpack.

LEARN BY SHARING

_____   I can say thank you when somebody gives me something.

_____   Actions.

_____   I can say please when I ask for something.

_____   Polite actions that I can do.

LEARN BY PRACTICING

Points

_____   Actions. ☐

_____   People can dream. ☐

_____   Actions people might do while they sleep. ☐

_____   People can snore. ☐

_____   Sports I watched during the winter Olympics. ☐

_____   I watched six ice hockey games. ☐

_____   I also watched downhill skiing events. ☐

_____   Sports. ☐

Learning Sheet 5A

LEARN BY WATCHING

Name _____

Date _____

Identifying Details When Given the Topic and Main Idea

INSTRUCTIONS:
Identify three appropriate details for the topic and main idea provided.

Topic		
SPORTS		
Main Idea		
Sports build character.		
Detail #1	Detail #2	Detail #3

Learning Sheet 5A

Name _____

Date _____

Identifying Details When Given the Topic and Main Idea

INSTRUCTIONS:
Identify three appropriate details for the topic and main idea provided.

Topic
MY ROOM

Main Idea
I love the way my room looks.

Detail #1	Detail #2	Detail #3

Learning Sheet 5A

LEARN BY PRACTICING

Identifying Details When Given the Topic and Main Idea

INSTRUCTIONS:
Identify three appropriate details for the topic and main idea provided.

Topic
BOOKS

Main Idea
My three favorite books

Detail #1 ☐	Detail #2 ☐	Detail #3 ☐

Learning Sheet 5A
LEARN BY PRACTICING

Identifying Details When Given the Topic and Main Idea

INSTRUCTIONS:
Identify three appropriate details for the topic and main idea provided.

Topic		
MY FUTURE		
Main Idea		
Three things I'd like to accomplish		
Detail #1 ☐	Detail #2 ☐	Detail #3 ☐

Learning Sheet 5B

LEARN BY WATCHING

Identifying Details When Given the Topic and Main Idea

INSTRUCTIONS:
Identify three appropriate details for the topic and main idea provided.

Topic		
RESPECT		
Main Idea		
We should show respect in several ways.		
Detail #1	Detail #2	Detail #3

Learning Sheet 5B

Name _____

Date _____

LEARN BY SHARING

Identifying Details When Given the Topic and Main Idea

INSTRUCTIONS:
Identify three appropriate details for the topic and main idea provided.

Topic		
HAVING FUN		
Main Idea		
An ideal night on the town		
Detail #1	Detail #2	Detail #3

Learning Sheet 5B

LEARN BY PRACTICING

Name _____

Date _____

Identifying Details When Given the Topic and Main Idea

INSTRUCTIONS:
Identify three appropriate details for the topic and main idea provided.

Topic
VACATIONS

Main Idea
My dream vacation

Detail #1 ☐	Detail #2 ☐	Detail #3 ☐

Learning Sheet 5B

LEARN BY PRACTICING

Identifying Details When Given the Topic and Main Idea

INSTRUCTIONS:
Identify three appropriate details for the topic and main idea provided.

Topic
LEARNING STRATEGIES

Main Idea
Strategies help you be a better student.

Detail #1 ☐	Detail #2 ☐	Detail #3 ☐

Learning Sheet 5C

LEARN BY WATCHING

Name _____

Date _____

Identifying Details When Given the Topic and Main Idea

INSTRUCTIONS:
Identify three appropriate details for the topic and main idea provided.

Topic		
THE ZOO		
Main Idea		
Frightening animals at the zoo		
Detail #1	Detail #2	Detail #3

Learning Sheet 5C

Name _____

Date _____

Identifying Details When Given the Topic and Main Idea

INSTRUCTIONS:
Identify three appropriate details for the topic and main idea provided.

Topic
COMPUTER SKILLS

Main Idea
I can do a lot on the computer.

Detail #1	Detail #2	Detail #3

Learning Sheet 5C

LEARN BY PRACTICING

Identifying Details When Given the Topic and Main Idea

INSTRUCTIONS:
Identify three appropriate details for the topic and main idea provided.

Topic		
MUSIC		
Main Idea		
My favorite recording artists		
Detail #1 ☐	Detail #2 ☐	Detail #3 ☐

Learning Sheet 5C

LEARN BY PRACTICING

Name _____

Date _____

Identifying Details When Given the Topic and Main Idea

INSTRUCTIONS:
Identify three appropriate details for the topic and main idea provided.

Topic		
CARTOON CHARACTERS		
Main Idea		
My favorite cartoon characters		
Detail #1 ☐	Detail #2 ☐	Detail #3 ☐

Learning Sheet 5D

LEARN BY WATCHING

Identifying Details When Given the Topic and Main Idea

INSTRUCTIONS:
Identify three appropriate details for the topic and main idea provided.

Topic
IDEAS

Main Idea
Important ideas I have learned

Detail #1	Detail #2	Detail #3

Learning Sheet 5D
LEARN BY SHARING

Identifying Details When Given the Topic and Main Idea

INSTRUCTIONS:
Identify three appropriate details for the topic and main idea provided.

Topic		
MY DOG		

Main Idea		
What I love about my dog		

Detail #1	Detail #2	Detail #3

Learning Sheet 5D

LEARN BY PRACTICING

Name _____

Date _____

Identifying Details When Given the Topic and Main Idea

INSTRUCTIONS:
Identify three appropriate details for the topic and main idea provided.

Topic		
GOALS		

Main Idea		
What I hope to achieve this year		

Detail #1	Detail #2	Detail #3
☐	☐	☐

Learning Sheet 5D

Name _____

Date _____

Identifying Details When Given the Topic and Main Idea

INSTRUCTIONS:
Identify three appropriate details for the topic and main idea provided.

| Topic |
| ATHLETES |

| Main Idea |
| My three favorite athletes |

| Detail #1 | Detail #2 | Detail #3 |
| ☐ | ☐ | ☐ |

Learning Sheet 6A

LEARN BY WATCHING

Name _____

Date _____

Identifying Details in Paragraphs

INSTRUCTIONS:
Identify three appropriate details in the paragraph below for the topic and main idea provided.

John F. Kennedy: America's Youngest President

John F. Kennedy, JFK, had a full life even before he became president. JFK was the second of nine children. As a young man, he loved sports and reading. He went to Harvard for his college education. During World War II, he was a war hero. He saved the lives of his crew on a shipwrecked cruiser, even though he himself was injured. JFK was awarded the Navy Marine Corps Medal for his bravery during the war. After he returned to America, he became a popular politician.

Topic		
JFK		
Main Idea		
JFK had a full life before he became president.		
Detail #1	Detail #2	Detail #3

Learning Sheet 6A

LEARN BY SHARING

Identifying Details in Paragraphs

INSTRUCTIONS:
Identify three appropriate details in the paragraph below for the topic and main idea provided.

John F. Kennedy: America's Youngest President (cont.)

During his short term in office, JFK accomplished a great deal. He started the Peace Corps program. The Peace Corps sent volunteers to work in countries where there were many poor people. Peace Corps volunteers helped with education, construction, farming, and healthcare. The president also started "Project Apollo." This project led to America putting a man on the moon. The president's greatest crisis occurred when the Soviet Union put nuclear missiles on the island of Cuba. JFK was determined to make sure that the Soviets removed the missiles. He ordered the U.S. Navy to surround Cuba. The Soviets realized the president was very serious and finally agreed to remove the missiles. A world crisis was avoided.

Topic
JFK

Main Idea
JFK accomplished a great deal as president.

Detail #1	Detail #2	Detail #3

Learning Sheet 6A
LEARN BY PRACTICING

Name _____

Date _____

Identifying Details in Paragraphs

INSTRUCTIONS:
Identify three appropriate details in the paragraph below for the topic and main idea provided.

John F. Kennedy: America's Youngest President (cont.)

Sadly, President Kennedy is remembered today for the way he died as much as for what he did while he was alive. On November 22, 1963, JFK went to Dallas to give political speeches. He drove through the city in a convertible and was shot with a rifle from an open window in a nearby building. Shortly afterwards, the police arrested Lee Harvey Oswald and charged him with killing the president. A few days after the arrest, however, Mr. Oswald was also murdered. For that reason, people will never fully know all the details about JFK's death. John F. Kennedy's funeral was watched on television by almost everyone in the United States. Many other people around the world also watched the funeral.

Topic		
JFK		
Main Idea		
JFK is remembered for his death.		
Detail #1 ☐	Detail #2 ☐	Detail #3 ☐

Learning Sheet 6B

LEARN BY WATCHING

Name _____

Date _____

Identifying Details in Paragraphs

INSTRUCTIONS:
Identify three appropriate details in the paragraph below for the topic and main idea provided.

The Great One Was Also the Creative One

    The greatest athlete of all time may have been Wayne Gretzky, a skinny young man from Canada. During his career as a hockey player in the NHL, Gretzky was clearly the best player in the league. Mr. Gretzky, who came to be known as the "Great One," set many, many records. He was the captain of the champion Edmonton Oilers, which some people consider the greatest hockey team ever. The Great One smashed the records for most goals and most assists in a career. Gretzky also set the record for most goals and assists in a season. He was so great that he even set the record for most records set by a player.

Topic
WAYNE GRETZKY

Main Idea
Gretzky may have been the greatest athlete of all time.

Detail #1	Detail #2	Detail #3

Learning Sheet 6B

LEARN BY SHARING

Name _____

Date _____

Identifying Details in Paragraphs

INSTRUCTIONS:
Identify three appropriate details in the paragraph below for the topic and main idea provided.

The Great One Was Also the Creative One (cont.)

As a hockey player, Gretzky's creative vision was very important. He seemed to see plays develop quicker than other players could. He made awesome passes to players because he could use his imagination to figure out what would happen next faster than others. He transformed hockey by turning the area behind the goal into an excellent place to set up goals. Rather than skating to where the puck was, Gretzky said he tried to skate to where the puck was going to be.

Topic		
WAYNE GRETZKY		
Main Idea		
Gretzky's creative vision was very important.		
Detail #1	Detail #2	Detail #3

Learning Sheet 6B
LEARN BY PRACTICING

Name _____

Date _____

Identifying Details in Paragraphs

INSTRUCTIONS:
Identify three appropriate details in the paragraph below for the topic and main idea provided.

The Great One Was Also the Creative One (cont.)

Gretzky's career shows everyone that creative vision and imagination can be just as important as talent. Being creative helps students write stories, create art, and make music. Also, using their imagination helps students see ideas from more than one perspective. What is true in school will also be true in life. Creative scientists are often the people who make the most important discoveries. Creative police officers find the best ways to stop crime. Creative people in all kinds of jobs are the ones who do the best work. In other words, to be successful, we can all learn from the Great One. By learning and practicing to be more creative, everyone has a chance to excel like Gretzky.

Topic
CREATIVITY AND IMAGINATION

Main Idea
Creativity is very important.

Detail #1 ☐	Detail #2 ☐	Detail #3 ☐

39

Learning Sheet 6C

Name _____

Date _____

LEARN BY WATCHING

Identifying Details in Paragraphs

INSTRUCTIONS:
Identify three appropriate details in the paragraph below for the topic and main idea provided.

Your Dream Can Make a Difference

On August 28, 1963, Dr. Martin Luther King made history. He did so by giving his now famous "I have a dream" speech. In that speech, Dr. King said that more than anything else he hoped for a time when all Americans were treated equally. He said that he dreamt for the day when black and white people would be able to "sit down together at a table of brotherhood." Dr. King's dream became the dream of many, many Americans. His speech and his goal are still alive in the hearts and minds of many Americans. We should remember his words as we face troubled times in the future.

Topic
DR. MARTIN LUTHER KING, JR.

Main Idea
MLK had an important dream.

Detail #1	Detail #2	Detail #3

Learning Sheet 6C

LEARN BY SHARING

Name _____

Date _____

Identifying Details in Paragraphs

INSTRUCTIONS:
Identify three appropriate details in the paragraph below for the topic and main idea provided.

Your Dream Can Make a Difference (cont.)

What the famous "I have a dream" speech shows is that people can make a difference in the world if they know what they want and go after it. A clear goal, forcefully stated and pursued, can make a difference. Dr. King really influenced civil rights. Other people have made a difference by dreaming of improvements to the environment, to women's lives, to education, to music, or to the arts. People who dream big dreams can make big changes occur. It happens every day.

Topic
PEOPLE CAN MAKE A DIFFERENCE

Main Idea
People can make a difference if they know their goals and pursue them.

Detail #1	Detail #2	Detail #3

Learning Sheet 6C

LEARN BY PRACTICING

Name _____

Date _____

Identifying Details in Paragraphs

INSTRUCTIONS:
Identify three appropriate details in the paragraph below for the topic and main idea provided.

Your Dream Can Make a Difference (cont.)

Sometimes, more than one person must be involved to make a dream come true. Dr. King recognized the power of organizations in bringing about change. He was president of the Montgomery Improvement Association, which sponsored the Montgomery Bus Boycott following the arrest of Rosa Parks. He founded the Southern Christian Leadership Conference and was its president from 1957 to 1968. He was also active as a teacher in the National Baptist Convention. Without the dedicated work of people in these organizations, racial equality might still be just a dream.

Topic
MLK

Main Idea
MLK recognized the power of organizations.

Detail #1 ☐	Detail #2 ☐	Detail #3 ☐

Learning Sheet 6D

Name _____

Date _____

LEARN BY WATCHING

Identifying Details in Paragraphs

INSTRUCTIONS:
Identify three appropriate details in the paragraph below for the topic and main idea provided.

Video Wars

Back before DVDs, there was a big battle to see which kind of videotape most people would use. One kind of videotape was made by Sony. It was called Betamax. The other kind of videotape was made by JVC. It was called VHS. Betamax suffered from a time disadvantage. The early Betamax systems had a high quality image, but they could only record for an hour. This was not long enough to hold a regular movie. The VHS companies produced a lower quality image, but the videotapes could record for two hours.

Topic		
VIDEO WARS		
Main Idea **Betamax and VHS competed for the videotape market.**		
Detail #1	Detail #2	Detail #3

Learning Sheet 6D

LEARN BY SHARING

Identifying Details in Paragraphs

INSTRUCTIONS:
Identify three appropriate details in the paragraph below for the topic and main idea provided.

Video Wars (cont.)

Cost of video players was another deciding factor. VHS players got an early lead in the market because you could rent them for a low fee. On the other hand, people had to buy their own Betamax players. These players cost about $2,600. By the time people could rent a Betamax player, VHS players already owned 70% of the market.

Topic
VIDEO WARS

Main Idea
The cost of video players was a deciding factor.

Detail #1	Detail #2	Detail #3

Learning Sheet 6D

LEARN BY PRACTICING

Name _____

Date _____

Identifying Details in Paragraphs

INSTRUCTIONS:
Identify three appropriate details in the paragraph below for the topic and main idea provided.

Video Wars (cont.)

The final factor was the availability of a wide variety of movies. Sony placed restrictions on the types of films that could be sold in Betamax format. The VHS companies placed no such restrictions on their tapes. As a result, Betamax had only a 25% market share in 1984, which was its best year. The Betamax share was down to 7.5% of the market in 1986.

Topic		
VIDEO WARS		
Main Idea		
Availablity of movies was another factor.		
Detail #1 ☐	Detail #2 ☐	Detail #3 ☐

Learning Sheet 7A

LEARN BY WATCHING

Identifying Topics, Main Ideas, and Details in Paragraphs

INSTRUCTIONS:
Use the TM-to-D process to identify the topic, main idea, and three details for the following paragraph.

College: You Can Do It If You Want

There are many reasons why young people want to go to college. Students understand that they need a college education to succeed in the career they want. Without a college diploma or degree, many students end up working for low pay, and their jobs are often boring. College gives students an opportunity to be exposed to new ideas. It challenges them to develop problem-solving and creative-thinking skills. College gives students a chance to meet new people from around the nation and the world. It teaches about new fields and introduces more choices for future careers.

Topic

Main Idea

Detail #1	Detail #2	Detail #3

Learning Sheet 7A

Name _____

LEARN BY SHARING

Date _____

Identifying Topics, Main Ideas, and Details in Paragraphs

INSTRUCTIONS:
Use the TM-to-D process to identify the topic, main idea, and three details for the following paragraph.

College: You Can Do It If You Want (cont.)

There are many ways for parents and students to find money for college. Tax credits reduce the amount of income tax parents pay so that children can go to college. There are also special tax-free savings accounts parents and grandparents can use for college tuition. The "HOPE Scholarship" can save parents or students money on their taxes. Financial aid provides scholarships, which do not have to be paid back. Government loans do have to be repaid, but the interest rates are very low. Federal Pell Grants also help students pay for their college education. Guidance counselors and teachers can help students learn more about financial aid.

Topic

Main Idea

Detail #1	Detail #2	Detail #3

Learning Sheet 7A

Name _____

Date _____

LEARN BY PRACTICING

Identifying Topics, Main Ideas, and Details in Paragraphs

INSTRUCTIONS:
Use the TM-to-D process to identify the topic, main idea, and three details for the following paragraph.

College: You Can Do It If You Want (cont.)

Students who want to go to college can do many things to prepare for success. Most important, they should work hard in high school. College students need reading, writing, and learning strategies to be effective. They also need to learn how to manage their time. Students can develop leadership skills through clubs and school activities. Those skills are important for success in college. Finally, students should set goals and explain their plans to teachers and parents. Well-planned goals and good academic skills can lead to college success.

Topic ☐		
Main Idea ☐		
Detail #1 ☐	Detail #2 ☐	Detail #3 ☐

Learning Sheet 7B

Name _____

LEARN BY WATCHING

Date _____

Identifying Topics, Main Ideas, and Details in Paragraphs

INSTRUCTIONS:
Use the TM-to-D process to identify the topic, main idea, and three details for the following paragraph.

Empathy: Learning How to Understand Others

Being understood is an important part of being happy. People feel unhappy when they do not feel understood. For example, a child who longs to tell her parent an important story might feel sad when her parent is too busy to listen. A teacher can feel bad when he realizes his students are not listening. Similarly, a person who tells a friend something really important can feel disappointed if he realizes his friend is not listening. Sometimes people feel angry and argue just because they do not take the time to understand another person.

Topic
Main Idea

Detail #1	Detail #2	Detail #3

Learning Sheet 7B

Name _____

LEARN BY SHARING

Date _____

Identifying Topics, Main Ideas, and Details in Paragraphs

INSTRUCTIONS:
Use the TM-to-D process to identify the topic, main idea, and three details for the following paragraph.

Empathy: Learning How to Understand Others (cont.)

Luckily, empathy, which is the skill of understanding others, is something we can learn. A good place to start is by listening carefully to what others are saying. We have to fully understand what another is saying before we speak. We can also use our imagination. Whenever we try to understand other people, we need to imagine all that goes on in their lives. For example, a student trying to understand her teacher might think about all the preparations the teacher has to do to present a lesson, how the teacher feels if students do not listen, and what pressures the teacher faces. To understand others, we have to imagine what others might be experiencing.

Topic

Main Idea

Detail #1	Detail #2	Detail #3

Learning Sheet 7B

Name _____

Date _____

LEARN BY PRACTICING
Identifying Topics, Main Ideas, and Details in Paragraphs

INSTRUCTIONS:
Use the TM-to-D process to identify the topic, main idea, and three details for the following paragraph.

Empathy: Learning How to Understand Others (cont.)

As we get better at understanding others, we will lead happier and richer lives. Sensitive people who understand others have a lot more friends than insensitive people. Sensitive people are seen as trustworthy and sympathetic, and people like to be with them. Also, people who are open to others' experiences lead more meaningful lives because they have a deeper understanding of people in general. People who are understanding are respected and appreciated, and those traits often lead to success in life.

Topic ☐
Main Idea ☐

Detail #1 ☐	Detail #2 ☐	Detail #3 ☐

Learning Sheet 7C

Name _____

LEARN BY WATCHING

Date _____

Identifying Topics, Main Ideas, and Details in Paragraphs

INSTRUCTIONS:
Use the TM-to-D process to identify the topic, main idea, and three details for the following paragraph.

Frangipani

Frangipani is a sweet-smelling, leafy plant that grows in the tropics. Known scientifically as plumeria, the plant is native to Mexico, Central America, and Venezuela. However, it has spread to many other countries and taken many other names. It is the national flower of both Laos and Nicaragua. In the Aztec language, the plant is called "crow flower." In Indonesia, it is called "temple tree," and in Australia it is called "dead man's fingers."

Topic
Main Idea

Detail #1	Detail #2	Detail #3

Learning Sheet 7C

Name _____

LEARN BY SHARING

Date _____

Identifying Topics, Main Ideas, and Details in Paragraphs

INSTRUCTIONS:
Use the TM-to-D process to identify the topic, main idea, and three details for the following paragraph.

Frangipani (cont.)

The word "frangipani" comes from Italy. "Frangipani" was the name of a powerful Roman family of the 11th, 12th, and 13th centuries. In the Italian language, frangipani means "breaker of bread." The family got that name because one of its members gave bread to poor people during a famine. The family's coat of arms (a symbol that we might call a "logo" today) shows two lions breaking apart a loaf of bread.

Topic

Main Idea

Detail #1	Detail #2	Detail #3

Learning Sheet 7C

Name _____

LEARN BY PRACTICING

Date _____

Identifying Topics, Main Ideas, and Details in Paragraphs

INSTRUCTIONS:
Use the TM-to-D process to identify the topic, main idea, and three details for the following paragraph.

Frangipani (cont.)

Today, when you smell that sweet frangipani flower, you are being taken back to 16th-century Italy. At that time, a noblewoman from the Frangipani family invented a perfume. It became a popular scent for women's gloves. When the plumeria flower was discovered in the tropics, its smell reminded people of the Italian glove perfume. That is why the name of the Frangipani family was given to the plant.

Topic ☐		
Main Idea ☐		
Detail #1 ☐	Detail #2 ☐	Detail #3 ☐

Learning Sheet 7D

Name _____

Date _____

LEARN BY WATCHING

Identifying Topics, Main Ideas, and Details in Paragraphs

INSTRUCTIONS:
Use the TM-to-D process to identify the topic, main idea, and three details for the following paragraph.

Recycling: One Way to Make a Difference

Recycling is one way to help our environment. The world's population is growing quickly. More and more people buy, use, and throw away more and more items. To make the books and papers we read, we chop down millions of trees each year. To create the cans that hold soft drinks, we remove minerals from the earth. We are also creating too much garbage. If we recycle, we can preserve minerals, trees, and oil supplies much longer. Businesses can reuse items and make new things out of discarded materials. Recycling also reduces the amount of garbage that is being dumped onto the earth.

Topic

Main Idea

Detail #1	Detail #2	Detail #3

Learning Sheet 7D

Name _____

Date _____

LEARN BY SHARING

Identifying Topics, Main Ideas, and Details in Paragraphs

INSTRUCTIONS:
Use the TM-to-D process to identify the topic, main idea, and three details for the following paragraph.

Recycling: One Way to Make a Difference (cont.)

People support recycling in many ways. Some towns and cities have special programs. In those places, people leave bottles, cans, and paper beside their trash for pickup. Often, they put those articles in a special blue box. City workers then gather up those items so that they can be recycled. Schools create programs so that paper and metal can be saved. Student programs involve recycling simple things like pop cans, photocopies, and newspapers. Many people also recycle on their own by saving materials at home and taking them to a recyling center. Some people make money by recycling newspapers, plastic items, and different types of cans.

Topic		
Main Idea		
Detail #1	Detail #2	Detail #3

Learning Sheet 7D

Name _____

LEARN BY PRACTICING

Date _____

Identifying Topics, Main Ideas, and Details in Paragraphs

INSTRUCTIONS:
Use the TM-to-D process to identify the topic, main idea, and three details for the following paragraph.

Recycling: One Way to Make a Difference (cont.)

Today, many everyday items contain reused materials. The roads we drive on, the carpets we walk on, and the benches we sit on can all be made from recycled products. In a typical home, paper towels, drink cans, bed sheets, and furniture can all be made from recycled products. We can support recycling just by buying products that are made from recycled materials. Every day, everyone can make a difference.

Topic ☐		
Main Idea ☐		
Detail #1 ☐	Detail #2 ☐	Detail #3 ☐

Learning Sheet 8A

Name _____

LEARN BY WATCHING
Paraphrasing the Main Idea and Details

Date _____

INSTRUCTIONS:
First, use the TM-to-D process to identify the topic, main idea, and three details in the paragraph below. Then, paraphrase the main idea and details on the lines below.

Jackie Robinson

      Jackie Robinson was both a great baseball player and a great man. Throughout his 10-year career in baseball, he compiled a .311 lifetime batting average, played in six World Series, and stole home 19 times. He was named Rookie of the Year in 1947 and MVP in 1949. All of these results would make any baseball player proud. Nevertheless, Jackie Robinson's greatest achievement was not with his bat or glove. Mr. Robinson will always be remembered as the first African-American man to play major league baseball.

Topic		
Main Idea		
Detail #1	**Detail #2**	**Detail #3**

Main idea: _____

_____

Detail 1:_____

_____

Detail 2:_____

_____

Detail 3:_____

_____

Learning Sheet 8A

Name _____

LEARN BY SHARING
Paraphrasing the Main Idea and Details

Date _____

INSTRUCTIONS:
First, use the TM-to-D process to identify the topic, main idea, and three details in the paragraph below. Then, paraphrase the main idea and details on the lines below.

Jackie Robinson (cont.)

Prior to 1947, major league baseball was segregated. This meant that only white players played in the major leagues. Black athletes could only play in the Negro Leagues. The Negro Leagues included great teams like the Kansas City Monarchs, the Hilldale Giants, and the Homestead Grays. Many amazing athletes like Satchel Paige, James "Cool Papa" Bell, and Pepper Bassett played in the Negro Leagues. These players were good enough to be major league stars, but they never got to play because they were black.

Topic		
Main Idea		
Detail #1	Detail #2	Detail #3

Main idea: _____

_____

Detail 1:_____

_____

Detail 2:_____

_____

Detail 3:_____

_____

Learning Sheet 8A

Name _____

LEARN BY PRACTICING
Paraphrasing the Main Idea and Details

Date _____

INSTRUCTIONS:
First, use the TM-to-D process to identify the topic, main idea, and three details in the paragraph below. Then, paraphrase the main idea and details on the lines below.

Jackie Robinson (cont.)

As the first black person to play on a major league baseball team, Jackie Robinson suffered a lot of abuse. At first, his own team threatened to go on strike to stop him from playing with them. Other players called him racially insulting names. Sometimes, pitchers threw baseballs at him to try to frighten him. Some so-called fans sent him death threats. Mr. Robinson resisted the temptation to strike back at those who attacked him. He rose above all of the personal attacks and stayed focused on being a great player. He won the respect of both fans and fellow players.

Topic ☐		
Main Idea ☐		
Detail #1 ☐	Detail #2 ☐	Detail #3 ☐

☐ Main idea: _____

_____

☐ Detail 1:_____

_____

☐ Detail 2:_____

_____

☐ Detail 3:_____

_____

Learning Sheet 8B

LEARN BY WATCHING

Paraphrasing the Main Idea and Details

INSTRUCTIONS:
First, use the TM-to-D process to identify the topic, main idea, and three details in the paragraph below. Then, paraphrase the main idea and details on the lines below.

What Does Your Body Say?

The way people move, smile, or dress often says more about them than the words they speak. Body language is the way we move our bodies when we talk. The body language of a speaker will effect how a class will react to the presentation. It can affect how people are seen by their friends. Using effective body language can even make a difference in getting an important job. People need to be aware of their body language.

Topic		
Main Idea		
Detail #1	Detail #2	Detail #3

Main idea: _____

_____

Detail 1:_____

_____

Detail 2:_____

_____

Detail 3:_____

_____

Learning Sheet 8B

Name _____

Date _____

LEARN BY SHARING
Paraphrasing the Main Idea and Details

INSTRUCTIONS:
First, use the TM-to-D process to identify the topic, main idea, and three details in the paragraph below. Then, paraphrase the main idea and details on the lines below.

What Does Your Body Say? (cont.)

Body language reveals your feelings in several ways. If you yawn, frown, or look away when someone is talking, your body is saying that you are not interested in the conversation. If you slouch down in a chair at your desk in school, your body tells everyone that you are not interested. If your clothes are sloppy or messy, your body language might show that you do not care about yourself. You need to pay careful attention to body language. If you want people to like, respect, or listen to you, you need to make sure you communicate positive feelings. Body language can show love or hatred, trust or suspicion, and confidence or fear.

Topic		
Main Idea		
Detail #1	**Detail #2**	**Detail #3**

Main idea: _____

_____

Detail 1:_____

_____

Detail 2:_____

_____

Detail 3:_____

_____

Learning Sheet 8B

Name _____

Date _____

LEARN BY PRACTICING
Paraphrasing the Main Idea and Details

INSTRUCTIONS:
First, use the TM-to-D process to identify the topic, main idea, and three details in the paragraph below. Then, paraphrase the main idea and details on the lines below.

What Does Your Body Say? (cont.)

      Several basic skills can help you use more effective body language. First, pay attention to other people's body language. Watch the way people around you communicate through their faces, their movements, and their clothing. Also, pay attention to how entertainers use their bodies to communicate. Actors spend years learning how to move in just the right way. Of course, you also need to pay attention to your own body language. Be sure to make eye contact when you are listening or talking. Be careful to wear clothes that show who you really are. If you pay attention to your body language, you should be able to communicate much more effectively.

Topic ☐
Main Idea ☐

Detail #1 ☐	Detail #2 ☐	Detail #3 ☐

☐ Main idea: _____

_____

☐ Detail 1:_____

_____

☐ Detail 2:_____

_____

☐ Detail 3:_____

_____

Learning Sheet 8C

LEARN BY WATCHING
Paraphrasing the Main Idea and Details

INSTRUCTIONS:
First, use the TM-to-D process to identify the topic, main idea, and three details in the paragraph below. Then, paraphrase the main idea and details on the lines below.

The Gift of Pain

Most people believe that pain is a bad experience. Pain can make us feel extremely uncomfortable. A headache can ruin an entire day. A broken bone can spoil several weeks or even months. Pain can also interfere with our ability to do things. A toothache can make eating ice cream impossible. A sprained ankle can stop someone from playing basketball. A stomachache can keep a student home from school. All in all, most people would agree that pain is a very negative part of life.

Topic		
Main Idea		
Detail #1	Detail #2	Detail #3

Main idea: _____

_____

Detail 1: _____

_____

Detail 2: _____

_____

Detail 3: _____

_____

Learning Sheet 8C

Name _____

LEARN BY SHARING
Paraphrasing the Main Idea and Details

Date _____

INSTRUCTIONS:
First, use the TM-to-D process to identify the topic, main idea, and three details in the paragraph below. Then, paraphrase the main idea and details on the lines below.

The Gift of Pain (cont.)

Dr. Paul Brand has spent a lot of time studying pain. In particular, he has worked with people who have leprosy. This is a tropical disease that damages skin and nerves. Leprosy, in its worst forms, can destroy people's hands, feet, or faces. Throughout history, leprosy has done such terrible damage that people with leprosy have been rejected by society. When he worked with patients with leprosy, Dr. Brand made an amazing discovery. He found that the main reason people with leprosy suffer is because they sometimes do not feel pain. Therefore, they can damage their bodies in all kinds of ways without even realizing they have done so.

Topic		
Main Idea		
Detail #1	**Detail #2**	**Detail #3**

Main idea: _____

_____

Detail 1:_____

_____

Detail 2:_____

_____

Detail 3:_____

_____

Learning Sheet 8C

Name _____

Date _____

LEARN BY PRACTICING
Paraphrasing the Main Idea & Details

INSTRUCTIONS:
First, use the TM-to-D process to identify the topic, main idea, and three details in the paragraph below. Then, paraphrase the main idea and details on the lines below.

The Gift of Pain (cont.)

In his book *The Gift of Pain*, Dr. Brand shows that pain is an important part of being healthy. Pain warns people that their bodies need attention. For example, a boy who feels a slight soreness in his eyes may notice a speck of dirt and wash it out. If he did not feel that pain, the speck of dirt might cause serious damage and lead to blindness. Similarly, a girl who feels a blister on her heel may bandage it for a few days until her foot is healthy again. If she did not heal the blister, she might get an infection and not be able to walk. The aches and pains of everyday life can be very uncomfortable. However, pain is a very important part of being healthy.

Topic ☐		
Main Idea ☐		
Detail #1 ☐	**Detail #2** ☐	**Detail #3** ☐

☐ Main idea: _____

_____

☐ Detail 1: _____

_____

☐ Detail 2: _____

_____

☐ Detail 3: _____

_____

Learning Sheet 8D

Name _____

LEARN BY WATCHING
Paraphrasing the Main Idea and Details

Date _____

INSTRUCTIONS:
First, use the TM-to-D process to identify the topic, main idea, and three details in the paragraph below. Then, paraphrase the main idea and details on the lines below.

Listening: The Heart of Communication

Many skills help you communicate. Some people say that to be a good communicator you need a clear voice. Others suggest that you should look right at the person when you talk. Certainly, thinking before you speak can help you convey your message. Also, be sure to choose your words carefully so people can understand you. More than anything else, however, to be a good communicator, you need to be a good listener.

Topic		
Main Idea		
Detail #1	**Detail #2**	**Detail #3**

Main idea: _____

_____

Detail 1: _____

_____

Detail 2: _____

_____

Detail 3: _____

_____

Learning Sheet 8D

Name _____

Date _____

LEARN BY SHARING
Paraphrasing the Main Idea and Details

INSTRUCTIONS:
First, use the TM-to-D process to identify the topic, main idea, and three details in the paragraph below. Then, paraphrase the main idea and details on the lines below.

Listening: The Heart of Communication (cont.)

Good listeners use many techniques to become better listeners. Good listeners start by truly wanting to hear what others have to say. They stop talking and take time to hear all of the words spoken. Good listeners also paraphrase. That means that they listen and then put a speaker's words into their own words. Sometimes good listeners check to make sure they understand what they think they have heard. They might ask questions that help them better understand what has been said. Really good listeners notice the emotions people show when they talk. They let a speaker know that they understand both the spoken words and the feelings that have been communicated.

Topic		
Main Idea		
Detail #1	Detail #2	Detail #3

Main idea: _____

_____

Detail 1:_____

_____

Detail 2:_____

_____

Detail 3:_____

_____

Learning Sheet 8D

Name _____

LEARN BY PRACTICING
Paraphrasing the Main Idea & Details

Date _____

INSTRUCTIONS:
First, use the TM-to-D process to identify the topic, main idea, and three details in the paragraph below. Then, paraphrase the main idea and details on the lines below.

Listening: The Heart of Communication (cont.)

Listening enhances communication in many ways. First, when you listen carefully, you show people that you think they are important. Listening is a sign of respect. When you do not listen, you suggest to people that their ideas do not matter. Second, listening builds trust. Listening intently to what a person says is the fastest way you can gain that person's trust. Third, listening enables you to learn a lot about what others think. If you know more about what others think, working together and solving problems becomes easier.

Topic ☐

Main Idea ☐

Detail #1 ☐	Detail #2 ☐	Detail #3 ☐

☐ Main idea: _____

_____

☐ Detail 1:_____

_____

☐ Detail 2:_____

_____

☐ Detail 3:_____

_____

Learning Sheet 9A
Paraphrasing Multiple Paragraphs

Name _____

Date _____

INSTRUCTIONS:
First, identify an appropriate topic, main idea, and relevant details for each paragraph. Then, paraphrase the main idea and two of the details for each paragraph on a *Paraphrasing Sheet*.

Helen Keller: Obstacles Can Be Overcome

Helen Keller suffered a great deal when she was a child. When she was 19 months old, she had an extremely high fever. Not sure what it was, her doctors called it "brain fever." Although the fever went away, it left a terrible mark. Right after the fever ended, Helen became blind. Very soon after that, she lost her hearing. Not surprisingly, Helen was incredibly frustrated. As a young child, she was very angry. She would kick and scream and smash dishes and lamps. She knew she was missing out on so much in life, but because she did not understand language, she did not fully understand what she was missing.

Helen's life changed when she met Anne Sullivan. Ms. Sullivan became Helen's tutor, and she taught her many, many important things. At first, Anne Sullivan taught Helen simple things like how to eat dinner politely and how to comb her hair. She also tried to teach Helen some simple words, like "cake" and "doll." Anne tried to teach her how to spell words by touching her hand. At first, she was not successful. However, when Anne took Helen to a well and taught her the word "water," Helen finally came to understand the meaning of words. In a few hours, Helen learned how to spell more than 30 words. She eventually learned to read Braille and write with a special typewriter. Helen learned so quickly that she became famous.

Helen Keller accomplished many great things, even though she could not see or hear. She went to Radcliffe College and was the first deaf-blind person to attend the college. She was also the first deaf-blind person to get a Bachelor's degree at the college. Anne and Helen went on many lecture tours together. Audiences were very interested in how Helen communicated. Helen worked hard to improve the conditions of blind people. She did not want people with disabilities to be treated better than others, just equally. She raised money to help people who were deaf or blind. She wrote several books that described her life and Anne Sullivan's role in her life. She became even more famous when her life was portrayed in the play and then the movie *The Miracle Worker*. Helen Keller's life proves that no matter what obstacles people face, they can still accomplish amazing things.

Learning Sheet 9B
Paraphrasing Multiple Paragraphs

Name _____

Date _____

INSTRUCTIONS:
First, identify an appropriate topic, main idea, and relevant details for each paragraph. Then, paraphrase the main idea and two of the details for each paragraph on a *Paraphrasing Sheet*.

Conflict: The Only Way to Talk?

Today's TV shows are filled with arguments. On daytime talk shows, unhappy couples are brought together and sometimes end up having real fights on TV. On reality TV programs, people viciously compete with each other to see who can win a large amount of money. On news shows, politicians argue about what is right for the country. TV dramas and sitcoms are no different: Parents and children, husbands and wives, boyfriends and girlfriends all seem to be arguing. If you only watched TV, you might think people never get along.

In reality, many people work hard to find respectful ways to talk to each other. TV does not paint a realistic picture of the way people communicate. Many individuals, even when they disagree, can resolve their differences without arguing. Talking without arguing is a valuable skill. People who can talk without getting upset are usually happier in life. They are also more successful on the job. Everyone can benefit from learning how to communicate without arguing. To get along, people do not have to give up their opinions. They just have to learn how to speak respectfully.

You can use several strategies to share your ideas without starting arguments. The first strategy is to really watch what you say when you speak. If you want to get along with people, you must avoid saying things that will upset them. Second, to avoid conflict, you must stop yourself from reacting to things other people say. Many people have learned to control themselves by simply counting to 10 before they talk back to someone who says something rude. Third, people often avoid conflict by making sure they do not blame others for their problems. If you know someone who is seldom critical and who accepts responsibility for his or her mistakes, you probably know a person who gets along well with others.

Learning Sheet 9C
Paraphrasing Multiple Paragraphs

Name _____

Date _____

INSTRUCTIONS:
First, identify an appropriate topic, main idea, and relevant details for each paragraph. Then, paraphrase the main idea and two of the details for each paragraph on a *Paraphrasing Sheet*.

Pay It Forward

Catherine Ryan Hyde has written a novel, *Pay It Forward*, that contains an idea that could change the world. The hero of her novel, Trevor, a 12-year-old boy, suggests that we could improve the world just by doing three favors for others. When those people want to pay back the favor, Trevor suggests that we ask them to "pay it forward." That is, people can "pay it forward" by doing three more favors for others. Then, those people can also pay it forward, and more and more people can get involved. At first there will be three favors, then each of those people will do favors, and then more and more and more people will do simple, good things.

Trevor's idea has inspired people all over the world. Now there is even a Pay It Forward Foundation. This foundation has been created to inspire young people to spread the "pay it forward" idea. In schools all over the world, students are making the world better. In Exeter, England, students are making school gardens and developing homework-help clubs. In Palm Bay, Florida, kindergarten students are making security blankets for children who are very sick. Students in South Bend, Indiana, visited the homes of people who needed help. The students cleaned up yards and did chores.

Now that you have read about the idea, you, too, can spread the word. You can learn more about "pay it forward" on the website www.payitforwardfoundation.org. You could suggest to your teachers that your class try to make "pay it forward" a project in your school. You could do three really good favors and ask others to "pay it forward." The purpose of Trevor's plan is to help people see that anyone can change the world. That is an idea all of us can share.

Learning Sheet 9D
Paraphrasing Multiple Paragraphs

Name _____

Date _____

INSTRUCTIONS:
First, identify an appropriate topic, main idea, and relevant details for each paragraph. Then, paraphrase the main idea and two of the details for each paragraph on a *Paraphrasing Sheet*.

Impressionist Art

When artists create a new style of painting, sometimes they find that people do not like their work. Some museum goers prefer to see familiar paintings. They do not like an artist to use light, color, or shape in an unusual way. They like to see paintings of human figures and outdoor scenes they recognize.

One group of painters who were not appreciated in their time were the Impressionists. They painted in France in the late 1800s. They took their name from how they painted. They used light and color and shadow. They did not focus on making a person or an outdoor scene look real. They painted an impression. The farther away you stood from the painting, the clearer it became. This upset viewers. They were not ready for this kind of painting.

One Impressionist artist who later became very famous was Claude Monet. He painted one church in the French city of Rouen many, many times. Each time he painted the church, he did so at a different time of day or in a new season. He showed how the light made the church look different in the morning or at night or in winter. Audiences were shocked at his paintings. They did not like them, and they would not buy them. Today, Monet's paintings, as well as many other Impressionist paintings, are the favorites of millions of people. People should remember that new art can be hard to understand. If people figure out what the artist wants them to see, they might appreciate the art more.

Learning Sheet 10A

LEARN BY WATCHING
Creating Topics and Main Ideas from Details

INSTRUCTIONS:
Identify an appropriate main idea and topic for each of the three details provided.

Topic		
Main Idea		
Detail #1	Detail #2	Detail #3
Making a new friend	Winning a big game	Getting a high grade

Learning Sheet 10A

Name _____

Date _____

LEARN BY SHARING
Creating Topics and Main Ideas from Details

INSTRUCTIONS:
Identify an appropriate main idea and topic for each of the three details provided.

Topic		
Main Idea		
Detail #1	Detail #2	Detail #3
Wash the dishes	Mow the lawn	Clean my room

Learning Sheet 10A

Name _____

LEARN BY PRACTICING
Creating Topics and Main Ideas from Details

Date _____

INSTRUCTIONS:
Identify an appropriate main idea and topic for each of the three details provided.

Topic
☐

Main Idea
☐

Detail #1	Detail #2	Detail #3
Kansas Jayhawks	**Kentucky Wildcats**	**Duke Bluedevils**

Learning Sheet 10A

Name _____

LEARN BY PRACTICING

Date _____

Creating Topics and Main Ideas from Details

INSTRUCTIONS:
Identify an appropriate main idea and topic for each of the three details provided.

Topic ☐		
Main Idea ☐		
Detail #1	Detail #2	Detail #3
Turkey	**Pumpkin pie**	**Dressing**

Learning Sheet 10B

LEARN BY WATCHING
Creating Topics and Main Ideas from Details

Name _____

Date _____

INSTRUCTIONS:
Identify an appropriate main idea and topic for each of the three details provided.

Topic
Main Idea

Detail #1	Detail #2	Detail #3
Handshake	High-five	Wave

Learning Sheet 10B

Name _____

Date _____

LEARN BY SHARING
Creating Topics and Main Ideas from Details

INSTRUCTIONS:
Identify an appropriate main idea and topic for each of the three details provided.

Topic

Main Idea

Detail #1	Detail #2	Detail #3
Hockey	Soccer	Lacrosse

Learning Sheet 10B

Name _____

LEARN BY PRACTICING
Creating Topics and Main Ideas from Details

Date _____

INSTRUCTIONS:
Identify an appropriate main idea and topic for each of the three details provided.

Topic ☐

Main Idea ☐

Detail #1	Detail #2	Detail #3
She hugs me	Wipes away my tears if I'm sad	Helps me with homework

Learning Sheet 10B

Name _____

Date _____

LEARN BY PRACTICING
Creating Topics and Main Ideas from Details

INSTRUCTIONS:
Identify an appropriate main idea and topic for each of the three details provided.

Topic ☐		
Main Idea ☐		
Detail #1	Detail #2	Detail #3
Cheesecake	Banana split	Apple pie

Learning Sheet 10C

Name _____

Date _____

LEARN BY WATCHING
Creating Topics and Main Ideas from Details

INSTRUCTIONS:
Identify an appropriate main idea and topic for each of the three details provided.

Topic

Main Idea

Detail #1	Detail #2	Detail #3
Ice cream sundaes	Barbequed hamburgers	Corn on the cob

Learning Sheet 10C

Name _____

LEARN BY SHARING

Date _____

Creating Topics and Main Ideas from Details

INSTRUCTIONS:
Identify an appropriate main idea and topic for each of the three details provided.

Topic
Main Idea

Detail #1	Detail #2	Detail #3
Mickey Mouse	**Daffy Duck**	**Scooby-Doo**

Learning Sheet 10C

LEARN BY PRACTICING
Creating Topics and Main Ideas from Details

INSTRUCTIONS:
Identify an appropriate main idea and topic for each of the three details provided.

Topic ☐

Main Idea ☐

Detail #1	Detail #2	Detail #3
Computers	Videogames	Skateboarding

Learning Sheet 10C

LEARN BY PRACTICING
Creating Topics and Main Ideas from Details

Name _____

Date _____

INSTRUCTIONS:
Identify an appropriate main idea and topic for each of the three details provided.

Topic ☐		
Main Idea ☐		
Detail #1	Detail #2	Detail #3
Planets	Stars	The moon

Learning Sheet 10D

Name _____

Date _____

LEARN BY WATCHING
Creating Topics and Main Ideas from Details

INSTRUCTIONS:
Identify an appropriate main idea and topic for each of the three details provided.

Topic		
Main Idea		
Detail #1	Detail #2	Detail #3
Eating a hotdog	Booing the umpire	Cheering for the home team

Learning Sheet 10D

Name _____

Date _____

LEARN BY SHARING
Creating Topics and Main Ideas from Details

INSTRUCTIONS:
Identify an appropriate main idea and topic for each of the three details provided.

Topic

Main Idea

Detail #1	Detail #2	Detail #3
Hurricanes	**Tornadoes**	**Earthquakes**

Learning Sheet 10D

LEARN BY PRACTICING
Creating Topics and Main Ideas from Details

INSTRUCTIONS:
Identify an appropriate main idea and topic for each of the three details provided.

Topic ☐		
Main Idea ☐		
Detail #1	Detail #2	Detail #3
Letting someone sit in your seat	Sharing your lunch	Helping someone with her work

Learning Sheet 10D

LEARN BY PRACTICING

Creating Topics and Main Ideas from Details

Name _____

Date _____

INSTRUCTIONS:
Identify an appropriate main idea and topic for each of the three details provided.

Topic ☐

Main Idea ☐

Detail #1	Detail #2	Detail #3
Watching TV	Listening to music	Playing videogames

Learning Sheet 11A

Name _____

Date _____

LEARN BY WATCHING
Identifying and Paraphrasing Details, Main Ideas, and Topics

INSTRUCTIONS:
First, identify three appropriate details, the main idea, and topic. Then, paraphrase the main idea and details on the lines below.

Rosa Parks: How One Person Made a Difference

In 1955, Rosa Parks was a 42-year-old African-American woman in Montgomery, Alabama. One December evening, she got onto a bus to ride home after work. At that time in Alabama, buses were segregated with seating up front reserved for white people. Since there were empty seats at the front of the bus, Rosa and other African-Americans sat down in the white section. Eventually, however, the bus filled up with white people. The bus driver shouted at the African-Americans on the bus to move to the back. Everyone moved back to the black section except Rosa Parks. She was tired of being mistreated.

Topic		
Main Idea		
Detail #1	Detail #2	Detail #3

Main idea: _____

_____

Detail 1:_____

_____

Detail 2:_____

_____

Detail 3:_____

_____

Learning Sheet 11A

Name _____

LEARN BY SHARING   Date _____
Identifying and Paraphrasing Details, Main Ideas, and Topics

INSTRUCTIONS:
First, identify three appropriate details, the main idea, and topic. Then, paraphrase the main idea and details on the lines below.

Rosa Parks: How One Person Made a Difference (cont.)

Mrs. Parks remembered the bus driver from 12 years earlier when he had forced her to enter through the back of the bus. Rosa decided that on this bus ride she was not going to be treated as a second-class citizen. She did not move. The bus driver angrily told her that the law said she had to move. In Montgomery, the law said that blacks were not even allowed to sit across the aisle from white people. Rosa Parks thought this was humiliating. She decided that she would not take such mistreatment any more. When the bus driver threatened that she would be arrested, she quietly stayed in her seat. In a short while, she was arrested and put in jail.

Topic		
Main Idea		
Detail #1	**Detail #2**	**Detail #3**

Main idea: _____

_____

Detail 1:_____

_____

Detail 2:_____

_____

Detail 3:_____

_____

Learning Sheet 11A

Name _____

LEARN BY PRACTICING

Date _____

Identifying and Paraphrasing Details, Main Ideas, and Topics

INSTRUCTIONS:

First, identify three appropriate details, the main idea, and topic. Then, paraphrase the main idea and details on the lines below.

Rosa Parks: How One Person Made a Difference (cont.)

Rosa Parks' friend E. D. Nixon paid her bail and organized black leaders in Alabama to support Rosa. They organized a boycott of all city buses. On December 5, 1955, African-Americans across the city of Montgomery refused to take the bus. The bus boycott continued for weeks and months. Since 75% of the passengers were black, the bus companies began to lose a lot of money. Eventually, the Supreme Court ruled that Montgomery's segregation laws were unconstitutional. The very next day, Rosa Parks, E. D. Nixon, and Martin Luther King Jr. boarded a city bus. Rosa took a seat in the front row.

Topic ☐		
Main Idea ☐		
Detail #1 ☐	**Detail #2** ☐	**Detail #3** ☐

☐ Main idea: _____

_____

☐ Detail 1:_____

_____

☐ Detail 2:_____

_____

☐ Detail 3:_____

_____

Learning Sheet 11B

Name _____

LEARN BY WATCHING

Date _____

Identifying and Paraphrasing Details, Main Ideas, and Topics

INSTRUCTIONS:

First, identify three appropriate details, the main idea, and topic. Then, paraphrase the main idea and details on the lines below.

Canada's Favorite Sport

In America, basketball and football are popular sports. In Canada, hockey is more popular than basketball and football combined! On just about any street corner during the summer, Canadian kids play various forms of the game. All that children need to play the game are a few friends, hockey sticks, a ball, and two hockey nets. They can play the game on any smooth surface, such as a parking lot, a paved school yard, or a driveway. Some children even play on tennis courts. Often, a net is not even required. Kids just set up shoes or boots as goal posts.

Topic

Main Idea

Detail #1	Detail #2	Detail #3

Main idea: _____

_____

Detail 1:_____

_____

Detail 2:_____

_____

Detail 3:_____

_____

Learning Sheet 11B

LEARN BY SHARING

Identifying and Paraphrasing Details, Main Ideas, and Topics

INSTRUCTIONS:
First, identify three appropriate details, the main idea, and topic. Then, paraphrase the main idea and details on the lines below.

Canada's Favorite Sport (cont.)

When the weather turns cold and the rivers and ponds freeze, children in Canada put away their running shoes and get out their ice skates. Now, instead of playing hockey on the pavement, they play on a clear patch of ice. To prepare the ice for hockey, children grab their snow shovels and scrape away the snow to create an area large enough for the game to be played. Sometimes, the piles of snow form walls around the natural hockey rink they have created. The game is usually played for hours. No one really keeps score. The puck is just skated back and forth on the bumpy ice.

Topic
Main Idea

Detail #1	Detail #2	Detail #3

Main idea: _____

_____

Detail 1:_____

_____

Detail 2:_____

_____

Detail 3:_____

_____

Learning Sheet 11B

LEARN BY PRACTICING

Identifying and Paraphrasing Details, Main Ideas, and Topics

INSTRUCTIONS:
First, identify three appropriate details, the main idea, and topic. Then, paraphrase the main idea and details on the lines below.

Canada's Favorite Sport (cont.)

In the past, ice hockey was played on almost every frozen creek and pond in the nation. Today, most ice hockey in Canada is played indoors. Indoors, hockey is a much different game. Players wear brightly colored jerseys, expensive helmets, gloves, and pads. Goalies wear heavy pads covering almost their whole body. They also wear masks to protect them from the pucks that are shot at them. Referees wear black-and-white striped jerseys. Parents, friends, and fans sit in the stands, cheering on their team. Whether it is played on a parking lot, a pond, or a smooth arena, hockey is enjoyed by millions of Canadians.

Topic ☐

Main Idea ☐

Detail #1 ☐	Detail #2 ☐	Detail #3 ☐

☐ Main idea: _____

_____

☐ Detail 1:_____

_____

☐ Detail 2:_____

_____

☐ Detail 3:_____

_____

Learning Sheet 11C

Name _____

LEARN BY WATCHING

Date _____

Identifying and Paraphrasing Details, Main Ideas, and Topics

INSTRUCTIONS:

First, identify three appropriate details, the main idea, and topic. Then, paraphrase the main idea and details on the lines below.

Voting

Voting is one of the most important duties a citizen has. A democracy is based on the idea that citizens select their leaders. When you vote, you are choosing someone to represent your viewpoint on important issues. If you vote, you will have a say in how your city, state, or country is run. When you vote, you tell leaders what your preferences are on issues like war and taxes.

Topic
Main Idea

Detail #1	Detail #2	Detail #3

Main idea: _____

_____

Detail 1:_____

_____

Detail 2:_____

_____

Detail 3:_____

_____

Learning Sheet 11C

Name _____

LEARN BY SHARING

Date _____

Identifying and Paraphrasing Details, Main Ideas, and Topics

INSTRUCTIONS:
First, identify three appropriate details, the main idea, and topic. Then, paraphrase the main idea and details on the lines below.

Voting (cont.)

Once people in the United States are 18 years old, they can register to vote. Many young people do not bother to vote because they do not think their votes will matter. However, this is not true. Sometimes, elections can be won by as few as five votes. A few votes can decide whether a school will get money for new teachers or for sports or music programs. Maybe a few votes will decide whether or not a school gets a new building. Sometimes, a few votes will decide whether or not more taxes will be collected.

Topic

Main Idea

Detail #1	Detail #2	Detail #3

Main idea: _____

_____

Detail 1:_____

_____

Detail 2:_____

_____

Detail 3:_____

_____

Learning Sheet 11C

Name _____

LEARN BY PRACTICING

Date _____

Identifying and Paraphrasing Details, Main Ideas, and Topics

INSTRUCTIONS:
First, identify three appropriate details, the main idea, and topic. Then, paraphrase the main idea and details on the lines below.

Voting (cont.)

Voting is very important worldwide. In parts of Africa, Iraq, and Afghanistan, however, some voters might be threatened. Others might be beaten or even shot while they are waiting in line to vote. Nevertheless, voting is so important to these people that they will put themselves in danger to be able to have a voice in their government. Fortunately, most people in the U.S. do not have to risk their lives to vote.

Topic ☐		
Main Idea ☐		
Detail #1 ☐	Detail #2 ☐	Detail #3 ☐

☐ Main idea: _____

_____

☐ Detail 1:_____

_____

☐ Detail 2:_____

_____

☐ Detail 3:_____

_____

Learning Sheet 11D

Name _____

Date _____

LEARN BY WATCHING
Identifying and Paraphrasing Details, Main Ideas, and Topics

INSTRUCTIONS:
First, identify three appropriate details, the main idea, and topic. Then, paraphrase the main idea and details on the lines below.

Mark Twain

Mark Twain, whose real name was Samuel Clemens, was born in 1836 to a large family in Hannibal, Missouri. He was a newspaper writer in New York City and California. For two weeks, he was a volunteer Confederate soldier during the Civil War. He was also a riverboat pilot on the Mississippi River. He was a prospector, trying to find silver in the Nevada mountains, but he never found any. What Mark Twain was most famous for, though, was his writing.

Topic

Main Idea

Detail #1	Detail #2	Detail #3

Main idea: _____

_____

Detail 1:_____

_____

Detail 2:_____

_____

Detail 3:_____

_____

Learning Sheet 11D

Name _____

Date _____

LEARN BY SHARING

Identifying and Paraphrasing Details, Main Ideas, and Topics

INSTRUCTIONS:

First, identify three appropriate details, the main idea, and topic. Then, paraphrase the main idea and details on the lines below.

Mark Twain (cont.)

Mark Twain was an extremely popular writer. He wrote newspaper articles, short stories, and novels—all of them humorous. His style was to use exaggeration and surprise to make people laugh. He liked to say the unexpected. For example, he said, "The dog is a gentleman; I hope to go to his heaven, not man's" and "If man could be crossed with the cat, it would improve man, but it would deteriorate the cat."

Topic		
Main Idea		
Detail #1	**Detail #2**	**Detail #3**

Main idea: _____

_____

Detail 1:_____

_____

Detail 2:_____

_____

Detail 3:_____

_____

Learning Sheet 11D

Name _____

LEARN BY PRACTICING

Date _____

Identifying and Paraphrasing Details, Main Ideas, and Topics

INSTRUCTIONS:
First, identify three appropriate details, the main idea, and topic. Then, paraphrase the main idea and details on the lines below.

Mark Twain (cont.)

Two of Mark Twain's novels, *Tom Sawyer* and *Huckleberry Finn*, made him famous. That is because the books captured the spirit of what was happening in America at the time. Both books described Mark Twain's years in Missouri. They also explained what was happening in America during the Civil War and the difficult times after the war. Jim, a main character in *Huckleberry Finn*, was a slave. Mark Twain used his gift of humor to criticize slavery and to protest the terrible treatment of blacks after the Civil War. Students still read Mark Twain's books because they teach so much about American life during those years of our history.

Topic ☐		
Main Idea ☐		
Detail #1 ☐	**Detail #2** ☐	**Detail #3** ☐

☐ Main idea: _____

_____

☐ Detail 1: _____

_____

☐ Detail 2: _____

_____

☐ Detail 3: _____

_____

Learning Sheet 12A
Paraphrasing Passages When Main Ideas Are Not Clear

Name _____

Date _____

INSTRUCTIONS:
First, identify the relevant details for each paragraph. Then, identify the main idea and topic. Complete this task by paraphrasing each paragraph's main idea and details on a *Paraphrasing Sheet*.

Courage

Are you courageous? When people think of courage, they often think of someone doing something amazing. A hero who risks his life to save someone else might be considered courageous. A soldier who fights hard in a war for a just cause might be considered courageous. Also, superstar athletes who give every ounce of their energy to win a big game might be thought to be courageous. A man or woman who does a great deed when others are frightened away can be said to be courageous.

Most people think courage involves doing something amazing. This is not always true. The dictionary tells us that courage is what people show when they remain firm in the face of difficult or frightening experiences. Certainly, risking your life to save someone else is courageous. However, courage can be shown in many other ways. Here are a few examples. A person who makes friends with someone who is unpopular shows courage. A person who chooses to criticize people who make racist jokes shows courage. Also, teenagers who refuse to use drugs, even though their friends do, show courage. Courage can be shown in many, many ways. Whenever people do the right thing, even though it might be difficult, they are showing courage.

Not everyone is born being courageous. To learn about courage, you first must become clear about what you believe. Ask yourself, "What do I really believe?" Do you believe in kindness towards others, treating people equally, and being healthy? Do you believe in other important principles? Once you understand your beliefs, you will have many chances to stand up for them. You do not need to be loud or rude. You do not need to be aggressive. You just have to live according to your beliefs. Once you do that, you will be as courageous as any hero, athlete, or soldier.

Learning Sheet 12B
Paraphrasing Passages When Main Ideas Are Not Clear

Name _____

Date _____

INSTRUCTIONS:
First, identify the relevant details for each paragraph. Then, identify the main idea and topic. Complete this task by paraphrasing each paragraph's main idea and details on a *Paraphrasing Sheet*.

Surfing Without Water

Many people worry about the safety of skateboards. Perhaps they do not need to worry. The boards used to have metal wheels, but now they have plastic wheels. The new wheels hold onto pavement better and do not tip the board as easily. The new skateboards also have a type of tape that is placed on the top of them. The tape helps skateboarders get a better grip on the board, so they can stay on it more easily.

Some people become highly skilled at skateboarding. Today, many skateboarders compete in serious events. In some competitions, skateboarders race to see who can go the fastest or farthest. In other competitions, skateboarders perform tricks. One of the most common tricks is a "hang ten." This is when a skateboard rider perches on the front end of the board. The trick is called a hang ten because in the position, the rider's toes are hanging over the front of the board. Other tricks include difficult turns on the boards and jump moves.

Skateboarders do not have to enter competitions to have fun. However, skateboarders can have accidents and get hurt. When an accident occurs, people are less likely to be hurt badly if they are wearing gloves and knee and elbow pads, and maybe even a helmet. Skateboards can also hurt people other than their riders. Because of this, skateboarders should not ride where people are walking. Skateboarders who ride safely can look forward to lots of surfing without water.

Learning Sheet 12C
Paraphrasing Passages When Main Ideas Are Not Clear

Name _____

Date _____

INSTRUCTIONS:
First, identify the relevant details for each paragraph. Then, identify the main idea and topic. Complete this task by paraphrasing each paragraph's main idea and details on a *Paraphrasing Sheet*.

Dog Bites

People are often unaware of the dangers dogs can pose to children. Jake was a black Labrador who was good-natured and trustworthy most of the time. Unfortunately, Jake bit his owners' 18-month-old daughter in the face. She required 10 stitches above her eye. In 1979, a pit bull terrier attacked an 8-year-old boy in Hollywood, Florida. He had to have a lot of operations to repair his nose, ears, and skin. Even worse, in Sydney, Australia, a pet pit bull terrier killed a baby while his mother was working in the house. She said she had left the baby alone with the dog "only for a moment."

Dog bites occur more frequently in America than people realize. The number of child injuries from dog bites is greater than all cases of measles, whooping cough, and mumps combined each year. Dog attacks are a common cause of serious face injuries in children. Of the 44,000 facial bites to children reported each year, 16,000 require plastic surgery.

People may fear the growling Weimaraner that they pass on the street, but that is not the place where most attacks occur. The typical attacker is usually not a stray dog but the family pet. The victims are usually not adults but children under the age of 10. Most bites occur not out in the open but while the dog is leashed, fenced, chained, or indoors. People are most likely to be bitten by their own dog or by the dog of a friend or neighbor.

Learning Sheet 12D

**Paraphrasing Passages When Main Ideas
Are Not Clear**

Name _____

Date _____

INSTRUCTIONS:
**First, identify the relevant details for each paragraph. Then, identify the main
idea and topic. Complete this task by paraphrasing each paragraph's main idea
and details on a *Paraphrasing Sheet*.**

The St. Francis Dam Disaster

When the St. Francis Dam in Southern California broke on the night of March 12, 1928, a wall of water poured into San Francisquito Canyon. The 125-foot flood wave carried 12 billion gallons of water across the farms and towns below. It crushed the heavy concrete walls of a hydroelectric plant. It damaged or destroyed the towns of Fillmore, Bardsdale, and Santa Paula, and it killed between 400 and 500 people.

The failure of the St. Francis Dam came as a shock, but maybe it should have been foreseen. In 1926 and 1927, while the lake behind the dam was filling with water, several cracks appeared in the dam. When the lake was completely filled in 1928, the dam's supervisor discovered new leaks. However, the dam's designer, William Mulholland, said not to worry about them; a few leaks were normal in every dam. Just four days before the dam's collapse, a construction crew was blasting very close to the dam to build a new road. This was dangerous because the east side of the dam was built on top of an ancient landslide.

Who was at fault in the St. Francis Dam disaster? The dam's designer, Mulholland, at first accepted all the blame. Later, he said that the dam had been sabotaged. Today, experts who have analyzed the accident give three structural reasons. First, they cite uplift, or movement of the earth underneath the dam caused by geological forces. Second, they say that the dam was built too high. Third, after analyzing concrete that remained after the break, they determined that not enough water was used to make the concrete.

Learning Sheet 13A
Practicing Paraphrasing

Name _____

Date _____

INSTRUCTIONS:
Use either the TM-to-D process or the D-to-MT process to identify each paragraph's topic, main idea, and details. Complete this task by paraphrasing each paragraph's main idea and details on a *Paraphrasing Sheet*.

The Wanderers

Some problems take a long time to solve. The problem of the planets was originally posed by the philosopher Plato around 2,400 years ago. Plato knew that all the stars traveled across the night sky in the same positions from one year to the next—except for some! At least five lights in the sky moved in odd paths that differed from all the other stars, but why? Plato called these lights "planets"—which means "wanderers"—because they did not seem to have fixed paths.

Two thousand years later, around 1600, a Polish monk named Copernicus solved the problem of the planets, at least in part. He had two important ideas that changed the science of astronomy. One idea was that the earth rotates once a day, and this made it look as if the stars were moving at night. His other idea was that the planets, along with the earth, travel around the sun. This idea accounted for the odd paths that Plato could not figure out.

Other early astronomers helped complete the solution begun by Copernicus. For example, Kepler and Galileo improved on Copernicus's ideas. Finally, in 1687 the English genius Isaac Newton published his laws of motion. Scientists could use Newton's laws to accurately predict the movement of the planets years or centuries ahead. With the development of space travel in the 20th century, people have been able to send orbiting and landing craft to every planet in the solar system.

Learning Sheet 13B
Practicing Paraphrasing

Name _____

Date _____

INSTRUCTIONS:
Use either the TM-to-D process or the D-to-MT process to identify each paragraph's topic, main idea, and details. Complete this task by paraphrasing each paragraph's main idea and details on a *Paraphrasing Sheet.*

Gorilla Woman

People can choose to study many different subjects. Dian Fossey is famous for her studies of mountain gorillas. For 13 years, she lived in the mountains of Rwanda, Africa, studying the animals. As the first person to study gorillas up close, Fossey sat near the gorillas and watched them every day for many years. Even though she was close, the gorillas did not mind. The gorillas trusted her. Fossey gained the gorillas' trust by acting like them. She would sit by them, pretend to eat leaves, and even make gorilla noises.

Fossey learned that when some male gorillas grow up, they leave their childhood families to begin their own families. Second, she learned that female gorillas take care of their offspring, and that some female gorillas are better mothers than others. Third, she learned that gorillas have their own personalities.

Today, not many mountain gorillas are left in Africa. They are in danger of dying out because so many are killed each year by poachers. Poachers are people who illegally hunt animals. Sometimes, poachers kill adult gorillas and cut off their hands or heads. Then they sell them to people who mount the heads on their walls and use the hands for decorations. Other times, poachers sell young gorillas to zoos. Fossey tried to protect the gorillas against poachers, but she was killed in 1982. Although her killer was never found, some people believe that poachers killed her.

Learning Sheet 13C

Practicing Paraphrasing

Name _____

Date _____

INSTRUCTIONS:
Use either the TM-to-D process or the D-to-MT process to identify each paragraph's topic, main idea, and details. Complete this task by paraphrasing each paragraph's main idea and details on a *Paraphrasing Sheet*.

The Rise of Hip Hop

Hip hop music, which is also called "rap," became popular because of its freedom, its difficulty, and the celebrity status that sometimes comes with it. It has no formal rules. People just need to be original and to keep their rhymes synchronized to the beat of the music. Rapping requires great skill and creativity. That is because people have to perform their rap from memory or make it up on the spur of the moment. Finally, the fans praise and admire a good rapper so much that he or she feels as famous as a TV star or a professional athlete.

Rap music grew out of reggae music and emcee parties in the 1970s. At that time, a disk jockey named Kool Herc moved from Jamaica to New York. At first, New Yorkers ignored the rhymes he spoke over recorded reggae music. Herc changed his music to popular instrumental songs, playing the same sections of a record over and over again. Later, at big parties, emcees like Kool Herc would often shout their rhymes over the recorded music.

The terms "rap" and "hip hop" are now used interchangeably. However, that was not always true. Rap came out of a hip hop culture that had other parts as well. Hip hop included graffiti art, break dancing, and emceeing (as rapping was first known). The expression "hip hop" originally meant a lifestyle that included its own language, fashions, and music. When break dancing and graffiti lost their popularity, people began to use "hip hop" as another term for "rap." Today, few people could explain the difference between the two.

Learning Sheet 13D
Practicing Paraphrasing

Name _____

Date _____

INSTRUCTIONS:
Use either the TM-to-D process or the D-to-MT process to identify each paragraph's topic, main idea, and details. Complete this task by paraphrasing each paragraph's main idea and details on a *Paraphrasing Sheet*.

Have Cell Phones Made Life Better?

People are talking on cell phones more and more around the world. In the United States, cell phone usage grew from 340,000 subscribers in 1985 to 158 million in 2005. Today, Americans spend an average of seven hours a month talking on their cell phones. That figure is low compared to some Asian countries, for example. One of the highest rates is in Israel, where 76% of the population has cell phones.

Cell phones have both psychological appeal and practical advantages. They are a status symbol and help people to feel special and important. Cell phones can also improve convenience and safety. In one country, people use them to switch on the heat while they are driving home. A cell phone user can call for help if her car breaks down, which is especially helpful at night. Travelers and children can phone home to assure their family that they have arrived safely at their destinations.

Cell phones can also cause problems. People who use their cell phones while driving are more likely to have accidents. Ringing cell phones often interrupt movies, church services, lectures, and concerts. People speaking on their cell phones in subways can ruin the peace of mind of other passengers. A questionnaire found that 59% of people would rather visit the dentist than sit next to someone using a cell phone. Rude cell phone users have sometimes been violently attacked, for example, with pepper spray by movie goers or by drivers who ram them with cars.

Learning Sheet 14A
Generalizing to Standarized Tests

Name _____

Date _____

INSTRUCTIONS:
Read the following passage and apply either the TM-to-D or D-to-MT process. Then code and answer the questions about the passage.

Talent Shows

Lots of popular singers launched their careers by appearing on TV talent shows. "American Idol" has been a very popular show, and millions of people have watched it. At least three of the show's winners have gone on to recording success. In a single week, Kelly Clarkson's first single went from number 52 to number 1 on the Billboard singles chart. Ruben Studdard's "Soulful" album sold 400,000 copies, and Fantasia Barrino's first album included hit singles such as "Baby Mama." She also starred in a TV movie.

Years before "American Idol," which started in 2002, the Arthur Godfrey "Talent Scouts" show gave nationwide exposure to relatively unknown artists. "Talent Scouts" started as a radio show in 1938. Ten years later, it became a TV show. In 1951 and 1952, it reached number 1 in the ratings and stayed in the top 10 throughout the 1950s. Godfrey's show gave a big lift to entertainers such as Pat Boone, Tony Bennett, Eddie Fisher, and Lenny Bruce. However, Godfrey let a couple of "big fish" get away. Godfrey would not put either Elvis Presley or Buddy Holly on his show.

Slightly older and equally as successful as "Talent Scouts" was "The Original Amateur Hour." This show also started in radio but then moved to television. It ran from 1935 through 1970. It had a one-year revival in 1992. During that year, Nick Carter, now of the Backstreet Boys, was discovered. The show brought fame to such pop singers as Frank Sinatra, Pat Boone, and Ann-Margret, as well as such opera greats as Beverly Sills, Maria Callas, and Robert Merrill.

Questions:

1. Which talent show winner starred in a TV movie?
   a. Kelly Clarkson
   b. Lenny Bruce
   c. Fantasia Barrino
   d. Ruben Studdard

2. Which sentence best describes this passage?
   a. "American Idol" is better than previous talent shows.
   b. Talent shows have been popular for almost 80 years.
   c. Elvis Presley and Buddy Holly faced prejudice.
   d. All talent shows got their start in radio.

3. Which singer appeared in two different talent shows?
   a. Elvis Presley
   b. Nick Carter
   c. Frank Sinatra
   d. Pat Boone

4. The author would probably agree with the following statement.
   a. Talent shows lost popularity in the fifties.
   b. Talent shows are here to stay.
   c. The best way to start a talent show is on the radio.
   d. The older shows were of better quality than "American Idol."

5. The author of this passage gives examples of ...
   a. Talent shows that failed.
   b. Singers whose careers were helped by a talent show.
   c. Dancers whose careers were helped by a talent show.
   d. Entertainers who went from rags to riches.

Learning Sheet 14B
Generalizing to Standarized Tests

Name _____

Date _____

INSTRUCTIONS:
Read the following passage and apply either the TM-to-D or D-to-MT process. Then code and answer the questions about the passage.

Storms Can Be a Hassle

Storms can be not only dangerous but also inconvenient. They may cause loss of electrical power. If the lights in your house do not work, you can not see your way around at night. If the TV and videogames do not work, you may be forced to entertain yourself with something boring. If the refrigerator stays off too long, the food in it will spoil.

Be careful when a thunderstorm comes to your neighborhood. Lightning may strike your telephone or cable TV lines. Be sure to stay off the phone during a thunderstorm. If lightning hits the phone line when you are talking on the phone, you could get a bad shock. You should also unplug your computer and any large entertainment devices.

After a storm, play it safe when you go outside. Even though you might not hear any thunder, dangerous situations can still exist. Tree limbs may be hanging by a thread and could fall on you. Power lines could be down. If you touch one, it could electrocute you. If there has been a snow storm, driving conditions will remain unsafe until the streets are plowed.

Questions

1. What is the author's reason for writing this passage?
   a. To provide basic information about what to do during a storm.
   b. To entertain the reader with terrifying possibilities.
   c. To provide basic information about lightning.
   d. To explain how much damage storms can do.

2. What should you do when a thunderstorm is going on?
   a. Unplug the computer.
   b. Unplug the refrigerator.
   c. Call your friends and tell them what is happening.
   d. Play computer games to stay calm.

3. With which statement would the author most likely agree?
   a. Being afraid of thunderstorms makes sense.
   b. As long as your parents are not worried about the storm, you can relax.
   c. Be sure to take storms seriously.
   d. Exploring after a big storm is a great thing to do.

4. Food will spoil if …
   a. A storm hits your neighborhood.
   b. You do not put it in the refrigerator.
   c. The power to your house goes off.
   d. The refrigerator stays off too long.

5. The main topic of this passage is …
   a. Inconveniences at home.
   b. Problems caused by a storm.
   c. Snow storm safety.
   d. Phone and computer safety.

Learning Sheet 14C

Generalizing to Standarized Tests

INSTRUCTIONS:
Read the following passage and apply either the TM-to-D or D-to-MT process. Then code and answer the questions about the passage.

Fast Food Myths

A fast food myth is an idea some people believe about fast foods that is not supported by scientific proof. You may hear strong opinions about fast foods from your parents or friends. Where did they get these opinions? They may have gotten their ideas about fast foods from TV talk shows. They may have gotten their ideas from reading about a diet fad. Even fast food advertising can sound reasonable and persuasive.

Watch out for fast food myths as you decide what to eat. If a food package says "all natural," you might think it is healthy to eat. Cheeseburgers look like a balanced meal because they have carbohydrates, protein, dairy products, and lettuce. Energy bars may seem like a reasonable substitute for a normal meal. However, neither of these foods might provide the nutrition that a person needs.

To avoid being a victim of a fast food myth, learn the truth behind the myths. Even if the label says "all natural," the food could still be loaded with sugar, fats, cholesterol, and other ingredients that can lead to health problems. Cheeseburgers are very high in salt, calories, and fats, so do not eat them very often. Finally, energy bars are not a substitute for fresh fruits and vegetables. They can pose just as much risk to your health as cookies and candy.

Questions:

1. A fast food myth is
   a. A story about ancient gods and what they ate.
   b. Something people say to make you sick.
   c. An opinion not based on scientific proof.
   d. A form of advertising.

2. What is the author's reason for writing this passage?
   a. To entertain.
   b. To inform.
   c. To frighten.
   d. To celebrate.

3. Which sentence best summarizes the passage?
   a. Finding the truth about fast foods is difficult.
   b. Diet fads are the source of most myths.
   c. You should always avoid sugar and fats.
   d. Many ideas we have about fast foods are actually myths.

4. This passage is mostly about …
   a. How to think more carefully about what you eat.
   b. What to tell people when they give you a fast food myth.
   c. What you should not eat at fast food restaurants.
   d. The best kinds of fast foods.

5. Energy bars …
   a. Are a reasonable substitute for a normal meal.
   b. Are okay if the package label says "all natural."
   c. Can substitute for fresh fruits and vegetables.
   d. May not be a substitute for a normal meal.

Learning Sheet 14D
Generalizing to Standarized Tests

Name _____

Date _____

INSTRUCTIONS:
Read the following passage and apply either the TM-to-D or D-to-MT process. Then code and answer the questions about the passage.

Monster Movies

Monster movies have been popular since the beginning of the motion picture industry. From the 1890s through the 1940s, audiences thrilled to stories of hunchbacks, vampires, mummies, werewolves, and, of course, Frankenstein (even though that name was not given to the creature in Mary Shelley's 1818 novel). Many of these movies were based on literature in the horror genre. This kind of story dated back at least to the American author Edgar Allen Poe, who wrote before the Civil War.

Aliens—that is, monsters from outer space—became a popular movie theme in the 1950s. In 1938, a Halloween radio drama presented an attack from Mars and drove hundreds of listeners to hysteria. This was followed by hundreds of movies based on the same idea. Some aliens came to colonize the earth. Others came to kidnap earth people and take them to other planets. In "The Day the Earth Stood Still," a good alien comes to save the earth from destroying itself.

Since the invention of atomic weapons in the 1940s, many monster movies have been based on the consequences of nuclear radiation. Japanese filmmakers featured giant birds, giant moths, and, of course, Godzilla, all of which came into being because of radiation or atomic explosions. In the U.S., the movie "Them" told the story of ferocious, gigantic ants. A gigantic squid appeared in "It Came From Beneath the Sea." Both of these monsters were the result of radiation, although no technical explanations were ever provided: too boring for a monster movie!

Questions:

1. Which sentence best summarizes the passage?
   a. Radiation was the original idea behind monster movies.
   b. People watch monster movies to forget their own worries.
   c. Monster movies have been popular in every chapter of film history.
   d. All aliens were portrayed as dangerous and evil.

2. The main idea of paragraph 2 is …
   a. Monster movies started in the 1950s.
   b. Some popular monster movies are based on aliens.
   c. Some monster movies are based on the effects of radiation.
   d. Some monster movies are based on earth creatures.

3. No technical explanations were given for radiation monsters because
   a. The filmmakers did not understand nuclear physics.
   b. It was still top-secret government information.
   c. People might try to copy the film and make their own monsters.
   d. They would be too boring.

4. Which of the following did you learn?
   a. Mary Shelley called her monster Frankenstein.
   b. "Godzilla" and "Them" were based on the same idea of monster creation.
   c. "The Day the Earth Stood Still" was about werewolves.
   d. An attack of Martians caused a mass panic in 1938.

5. The author organizes the passage according to …
   a. Geographical locations.
   b. Historical periods.
   c. Age of film goers.
   d. How much money the movies made.

Posttest Passage

Name _____

Date _____

INSTRUCTIONS:
First, identify an appropriate main idea, topic, and relevant details for each paragraph. Then, paraphrase the main idea and two of the details for each paragraph on a *Paraphrasing Sheet*.

Gandhi: One of Our Greatest Leaders

A tiny man who weighed little more than 110 pounds came to be one of the most famous people in the world. Mahatma Gandhi, in many ways, lived the simplest of lives. Everything he owned could fit into one small sack. He wore simple clothes that looked like rags to most people. Each day he meditated on religious texts. He took a vow of chastity. He spent hours each day spinning yarn on a spinning wheel. He ate the simplest meals possible. He had to walk with the help of a crutch. He spent more than 2,000 days in jail. Nevertheless, he inspired many, many great leaders all over the world. Although he was opposed to bloodshed of any kind, he led the largest revolution in the history of the world.

As a young man, Gandhi was treated unjustly simply because of the color of his skin. His early experiences with prejudice shaped him, and Gandhi dedicated his life to fighting any kind of injustice. However, he fought against unfairness in a unique way. Gandhi strongly believed that people should not do a wrong action to create a right solution. For that reason, he was totally opposed to violence of any kind. He did not believe anyone should ever fight violence with violence. Instead, Gandhi proposed civil disobedience. He suggested that people could change the world by protesting, by striking, and by refusing to participate in anything that is unfair. This kind of protest required great courage, but Gandhi also believed it was the only moral way to make changes occur.

Gandhi's impact on the world is immense. In India, he led the people of his country to stand up for their rights. Without using any violence, they stood up to one of the strongest governments in the world. Eventually, India became a free country because of the revolution led by Gandhi. Gandhi may have had an even greater impact on the rest of the world. For example, Dr. Martin Luther King Jr. said that Gandhi greatly influenced him. Dr. King's firm belief in nonviolence is a direct result of his knowledge of Gandhi. In this way, Gandhi left a very significant mark on America's civil rights movement. More recently, Nelson Mandela, who overcame years and years of prejudice in South Africa, also said that Gandhi was a major influence on him. Clearly, Gandhi has touched the lives of many people in the world. Not only did he change his own country, but also through his deep commitment to a life of truth and justice, Gandhi inspired many great thinkers in the world, and he has freed many people from oppression.

Blank
Learning Sheets

Learning Sheet 1____

Name _____

Date _____

Paraphrasing Words

INSTRUCTIONS:
Paraphrase each word by writing it in your own words in the space provided.

EXAMPLES:

1. Awful ____terrible____   2. Frequently ____often____   3. Piece _____bit_____

LEARN BY WATCHING
C

☐ 1. _____ _____

☐ 2. _____ _____

☐ 3. _____ _____

LEARN BY SHARING
C

☐ 1. _____ _____

☐ 2. _____ _____

☐ 3. _____ _____

☐ 4. _____ _____

☐ 5. _____ _____

LEARN BY PRACTICING
C   Points

☐ 1. _____ _____ ☐

☐ 2. _____ _____ ☐

☐ 3. _____ _____ ☐

☐ 4. _____ _____ ☐

☐ 5. _____ _____ ☐

Learning Sheet 2___

Paraphrasing Phrases

Name _____

Date _____

INSTRUCTIONS:
Paraphrase each phrase by writing it in your own words in the space provided.

EXAMPLE:

a cool dude _____*a nice guy*_____

LEARN BY WATCHING
C   O   M

☐ ☐ ☐   1. _____
_____

☐ ☐ ☐   2. _____
_____

☐ ☐ ☐   3. _____
_____

LEARN BY SHARING
C   O   M

☐ ☐ ☐   1. _____
_____

☐ ☐ ☐   2. _____
_____

☐ ☐ ☐   3. _____
_____

LEARN BY PRACTICING
C   O   M

Poin

☐ ☐ ☐   1. _____
_____ ☐

☐ ☐ ☐   2. _____
_____ ☐

☐ ☐ ☐   3. _____
_____ ☐

☐ ☐ ☐   4. _____
_____ ☐

☐ ☐ ☐   5. _____
_____ ☐

Learning Sheet 3___

Paraphrasing Sentences

Name _____

Date _____

INSTRUCTIONS:
Paraphrase each sentence by writing it in your own words in the space provided.

EXAMPLE:
The boy was overjoyed. _The young man was exceedingly happy._

LEARN BY WATCHING

C O M

☐ ☐ ☐ 1. _____

☐ ☐ ☐ 2. _____

☐ ☐ ☐ 3. _____

LEARN BY SHARING

C O M

☐ ☐ ☐ 1. _____

☐ ☐ ☐ 2. _____

☐ ☐ ☐ 3. _____

LEARN BY PRACTICING

C O M   Points

☐ ☐ ☐ 1. _____ ☐

☐ ☐ ☐ 2. _____ ☐

☐ ☐ ☐ 3. _____ ☐

☐ ☐ ☐ 4. _____ ☐

☐ ☐ ☐ 5. _____ ☐

Learning Sheet 4___

Name _____

Identifying Topics, Main Ideas and Details

Date _____

INSTRUCTIONS:

Put a D beside each detail, a T beside each topic, and an M beside each main idea.

EXAMPLE:

D   The lead guitarist was fantastic.

T   The band.

M   The band played really well.

D   The drummer kept everyone playing right in time.

LEARN BY WATCHING

_____   _____

_____   _____

_____   _____

_____   _____

LEARN BY SHARING

_____   _____

_____   _____

_____   _____

_____   _____

LEARN BY PRACTICING

Points

_____   _____ ☐

_____   _____ ☐

_____   _____ ☐

_____   _____ ☐

_____   _____ ☐

_____   _____ ☐

_____   _____ ☐

_____   _____ ☐

Learning Sheet 5____

LEARN BY _____

Identifying Details When Given the Topic and Main Idea

INSTRUCTIONS:
Identify three appropriate details for the topic and main idea provided.

Topic
_____

Main Idea
_____

Detail #1	Detail #2	Detail #3

Learning Sheet 6____

Name _____

LEARN BY _____

Date _____

Identifying Details in Paragraphs

INSTRUCTIONS:
Identify three appropriate details in the paragraph below for the topic and main idea provided.

Topic		
_____		
Main Idea		
_____		
Detail #1	Detail #2	Detail #3

Learning Sheet 7____

Name _____

LEARN BY _____

Date _____

Identifying Topics, Main Ideas, and Details in Paragraphs

INSTRUCTIONS:
Use the TM-to-D process to identify the topic, main idea, and three details for the following paragraph.

Topic

Main Idea

Detail #1	Detail #2	Detail #3

Learning Sheet 8____

Name _____

Date _____

LEARN BY _____

Paraphrasing the Main Idea & Details

INSTRUCTIONS:
First, use the TM-to-D process to identify the topic, main idea, and three details in the paragraph below. Then, paraphrase the main idea and details on the lines below.

Topic		
Main Idea		
Detail #1	Detail #2	Detail #3

Main idea: _____

_____

Detail 1: _____

_____

Detail 2: _____

_____

Detail 3: _____

_____

Learning Sheet 9____

Paraphrasing Multiple Paragraphs

Name _____

Date _____

INSTRUCTIONS:
First, identify an appropriate topic, main idea, and relevant details for each paragraph. Then, paraphrase the main idea and two of the details for each paragraph on a *Paraphrasing Sheet*.

Learning Sheet 10____

Name _____

Date _____

LEARN BY _____

Creating Topics and Main Ideas from Details

INSTRUCTIONS:
Identify an appropriate main idea and topic for each of the three details provided.

Topic
Main Idea

Detail #1	Detail #2	Detail #3
_____	_____	_____
_____	_____	_____

Learning Sheet 11____

Name _____

LEARN BY _____

Date _____

Identifying and Paraphrasing Details, Main Ideas, and Topics

INSTRUCTIONS:

First, identify three appropriate details, the main idea, and topic in the paragraph below. Then, paraphrase the main idea and details on the lines below.

Topic
Main Idea

Detail #1	Detail #2	Detail #3

Main idea: _____

_____

Detail 1:_____

_____

Detail 2:_____

_____

Detail 3:_____

_____

Learning Sheet 12____

Name _____

Date _____

**Paraphrasing Passages When Main Ideas
Are Not Clear**

INSTRUCTIONS:
First, identify the relevant details for each paragraph. Then, identify the topic and main idea. Complete this task by paraphrasing each paragraph's main idea and details on a *Paraphrasing Sheet*.

Learning Sheet 13___

Practicing Paraphrasing

Name _____

Date _____

INSTRUCTIONS:

Use either the TM-to-D process or the D-to-MT process to identify each paragraph's topic, main idea, and details. Complete this task by paraphrasing each paragraph's main idea and details on a *Paraphrasing Sheet*.

Learning Sheet 14____

Generalizing to Standarized Tests

Name _____

Date _____

INSTRUCTIONS:
Read the following passage and apply either the TM-to-D or D-to-MT process. Then code and answer the questions about the passage.

Passage:

Questions: